Adventures in Courage:

THE SKYMASTERS

Adventures in Courage:

THE SKYMASTERS

BY DENNIS BRENNAN

Reilly & Lee • Chicago

To three other Brennans:
Cathy, Kevin and Sam

Copyright © 1968 by REILLY & LEE, *Division of Henry Regnery Co.*
Manufactured in the United States of America
LIBRARY OF CONGRESS CATALOG CARD NO. 68-18482

Table of Contents

Introduction

"How is your attitude, Gordo?"

"Real great."

"Good show, boy. Looks like you came out right on the money, on time."

This brief conversation took place on May 15, 1963, between American astronauts John Glenn and Gordon Cooper. Glenn was stationed aboard the U.S.S. *Coastal Sentry* some 275 miles south of Japan. Gordon Cooper was just completing the last of twenty-two orbits around the earth in the space capsule *Faith Seven*.

The original flight plan had called for the capsule to re-enter the earth's atmosphere under control of the capsule's automatic pilot system. But a failure in the ship's electrical system knocked the auto-pilot out of order. Cooper would have to control the re-entry of the *Faith Seven* manually. A mistake meant death if the capsule plunged into the atmosphere too quickly and burned.

Cooper made the re-entry successfully. Shortly afterwards he landed in the Pacific Ocean just three miles from the aircraft carrier, the U.S.S. *Kearsarge,* which had been waiting to pick him up.

Just after it was decided that Cooper must control the re-entry himself, he and Glenn exchanged radio reports on what procedures must be followed. To make sure that *Faith Seven* was in the proper position for Cooper to fire his re-entry rockets, he had to line up marks on the capsule's windows with the horizon and with predetermined stars. This he did.

"How does it check?" Glenn asked.

"Right on the old gazoo," Cooper replied.

In the face of deadly danger, Gordon Cooper was responding with cool determination.

He was flying in an ultra-scientifically engineered space capsule. Early aviation pioneers often flew in flimsy contraptions sometimes held together by nothing more than baling wire and prayer. Cooper and the early pioneers had, above all else, two things in common—a love of flight and a willingness to face the unknown.

The union of these two characteristics has filled the history of aviation with dramatic stories of men and women who have pitted their lives against an awesome and vast unknown—the world of flight.

Some of the early aviation pioneers whose adventures are told in this book gained fame that lasted only a short while. Others became so famous that the tales of their exploits are legendary. But famous or forgotten, they all possessed an almost religious belief that man is not necessarily an earthbound creature.

They also possessed the one necessary thing to make mankind the master of the sky as well as of the earth.

So that birds might fly, nature gave them wings.

So that man might fly, nature gave him courage.

Part I

In the Beginning, Balloons

The Papermakers of Annonay

Etienne Montgolfier was annoyed. It was time to start work and Joseph, his brother, had not yet appeared. Etienne sighed and walked into the shop. It was here that he and Joseph manufactured the finest quality paper that could be made in the eighteenth century.

Joseph and Etienne were descendents of an ancient paper-making family. Their ancestors had introduced paper into Jerusalem several centuries before, and their father was the first to make vellum paper in Great Britain. Now, with several centuries of tradition behind them, Joseph and Etienne continued with their family's work.

But Joseph. Ah, Joseph, Etienne sighed again. Lately his brother had not kept his mind on their work. In recent weeks, Etienne had scolded Joseph several times for neglecting his duties. This was strange, too, because Joseph was the older of the two men and should have been more responsible. Joseph, born in 1740, was now forty-three years old. Etienne was five years younger.

Etienne had given up his search as he returned to the shop.

11

There, before the fireplace, sat Joseph. It was winter and cold weather had already gripped their town of Annonay, a small village near Lyons, France.

Joseph sat before the fireplace staring as though hypnotized at the flames and smoke roaring up the chimney.

"So here you are," Etienne said. "I've been looking for you. It's time to go to work."

Joseph was startled by the sound of his brother's voice. He smiled sheepishly. In his lap was an open book which lay face down. Etienne could read the title from where he stood: *Experiments Relating to the Different Kinds of Air* by Joseph Priestly.

So that was it. Etienne shook his head. Joseph had been carrying this book around for several weeks. This was not the first time he had neglected his work to read it.

Not that Etienne wasn't interested in scientific things. This was most certainly not the case. He and Joseph shared a common interest in the world around them, although Joseph went about it more vigorously. He had already invented the lamp chimney and the hydraulic press.

Joseph spoke before Etienne had the chance to remind him again that it was time to go to work.

"Forgive me, brother," he said. "I have been sitting here watching the smoke rise up the chimney." He paused. "I am wondering what gases the fire must release in order to make the smoke go up."

"What about it?" Etienne replied.

Joseph began thinking aloud. "We know that smoke is lighter than the air. That's why it rises. I have been sitting here wondering if we could not capture some of the smoke in one of our paper sacks. Then, when we release the sack, the smoke inside should make it rise. What do you think?"

In spite of his desire to start work, the idea intrigued Etienne. It might work.

"I'm sure it would," he said. "Let's try it."

Caught up by the unique possibilities of the idea, the brothers began to search their shop for a paper sack that would do the job. It should be of finest quality and tightly made so that the smoke could not seep through. Soon they found one they thought would be suitable. By now, Etienne was so engrossed with the idea that he dismissed the idea of work for the day.

They returned to the fireplace and raked hot coals onto the shop's stone floor and then held the paper sack over them. They watched as smoke and hot fumes rose into the bag. Joseph put a small amount of straw onto the coals and they smiled in satisfaction as the amount of smoke doubled. They did not realize that it was the heat of the smoke and not the smoke itself which was lighter than the air.

"Well," Etienne said after a while, "it seems to be full of smoke. Shall we try?"

They released the sack. It hovered in midair for a second. Then it began to rise gently. In a moment it bumped the ceiling of the shop. Then it turned over and fell back to the floor, leaving behind a wispy trail of smoke.

"It works!" Joseph cried.

Delighted by the results of the test, they decided to go outside and make further tests using a larger sack. But their first experiment ended in failure. A gust of wind caught the sack and turned it upside down. The smoke poured out and it fell to the ground.

The brothers were not discouraged. "We must balance it," Joseph said. "We must hang weights from the mouth of the sack so it won't turn over."

Etienne ran into the shop and returned with a candle holder. They used strings to attach the holder to the sack's bottom. Once again they filled the sack with smoke.

"All right," said Joseph. "Let it go."

Immediately the sack began to rise. When it reached an altitude of about thirty feet it began to drift with the wind, slowly settling back to the ground. Laughing, the Montgolfier brothers chased it until it landed. The first hot-air balloon had flown.

They were surprised to discover that most of the smoke was still in the sack. They could not understand why, if the smoke was still there, the bag had fallen.

Joseph knew the answer.

"The smoke is cold," he said. "It must be hot in order to rise. We shall make another test. This time, after the sack is full of smoke, we will hang a brazier from it instead of the candle holder. We can put hot coals on the brazier and they will keep the smoke hot."

Etienne agreed that it sounded possible, and they prepared the brazier.

To their great delight this one rose higher than the first and remained aloft even longer. The experiment was a success. They still did not realize, however, that it was the hot air and not the smoke which made the sack rise.

But to the brothers who stood on that chilly November day in 1782 and watched their improvised "balloon" float gracefully through the air, it was not particularly important what made it rise. It *did* rise, and both realized the importance of their discovery.

They made several more tests that day. When they finally went to bed that night, neither could go to sleep easily. Their discovery had opened a whole new world for mankind.

Now, man might be able to achieve a dream that had begun when the first man looked skyward to envy the flight of a bird. The creatures of the sky must now share their world. Mankind was no longer earthbound.

But the enterprising Montgolfier brothers were not through. They had only just begun. Through the winter of 1782–83 they continued their experiments with balloons. Their first large-scale hot-air balloon, made of linen, measured 35 feet in diameter. An accident occurred on their first test with this new aircraft. It broke loose from its mooring lines and soared into the sky. The brothers watched with a mixture of awe and pleasure as it soared more than a thousand feet into the air.

It landed more than a mile from its starting point and was seen by a farmer who spread the word that the brothers were doing wondrous things with a "flying machine." Soon everyone began to ask Joseph and Etienne what they were doing, but they would just smile and reply: "Wait and see. Wait and see."

On June 5, 1783, the brothers made their first public demonstration, and it was a huge success. Word of their accomplishment was carried to every small town in France, and soon their names were known in every part of the European continent.

Throughout the summer of 1783 the Montgolfiers continued to work and soon had constructed a balloon measuring 75 feet in diameter. The tests they made with this giant-size model were highly successful and made even more spectacular flights than their other airships.

Eventually news of the brothers' newest balloon reached King Louis XVI of France. He asked Joseph and Etienne to make a special demonstration for himself and his queen,

Marie Antoinette. The brothers agreed, but four days before the special show the 75-foot balloon was destroyed in a storm.

Not discouraged, the enterprising brothers set about building another, smaller model. They finished it the morning of the demonstration before the King.

On September 19, 1783, the King and Queen and members of the royal court took their seats in the gardens of the Palace of Versailles, the royal residence where the demonstration was to be held. There, in the center of the garden, was the balloon. It was painted blue and decorated brightly. But this one was different from others the brothers had constructed. Around its bottom was a tub-like construction which they called a "gallery."

Louis XVI was curious about the gallery. "Tell us what that is," he told Joseph. "Can it be myself and my court are going to witness some person occupy this suspended platform during the flight?"

The two brothers grinned broadly. They had, indeed, prepared a special showing for him.

"That is our plan for a future ascent," said Joseph, "if the creatures we have brought with us today survive this particular demonstration."

"Creatures?" asked the puzzled King. "What kind of creatures?"

Etienne had been standing near a slatted box covered with a canvas. He removed the canvas, reached in, and brought out three very nervous animals—a rooster, a duck, and a bleating lamb.

The crowd murmured as Joseph and Etienne brought the animals to the balloon and tied them into the gallery with strings. By now the balloon was fully inflated and tugging strongly at the mooring lines which held it to the earth.

"Release it," Joseph cried to assistants holding the ropes. The crowd gasped as the aircraft instantly rose into the air. The curious symphony of bleats, crowing, and quacking from the three passengers became faint as the balloon climbed higher. It stayed aloft for eight minutes, and when it landed everyone rushed to see the condition of its passengers—the first land creatures to leave the earth's surface.

Happily, no one seemed more pleased about their safe return than the three passengers themselves. The rooster crowed, the duck quacked, and the lamb bleated louder than ever.

The King was ecstatic.

"Marvelous," he said, "simply marvelous! Oh, if it had only been I, instead of these dumb animals, to witness the view they must have seen."

"Your Majesty," Joseph said, "within the year you may do that very thing. My brother and I are planning to build a larger machine with a larger gallery, one that can carry you to a rare sight which you will be the first living person to experience."

History does not accord King Louis XVI of France any great amount of courage, and certainly his reaction to Joseph's offer was *not* what might have been expected from a brave man.

He thought it over for a moment. "It might be better," he said, "that another person—some worthless vagabond, for instance—should be the first man to take such a risky chance.

"I know! I shall designate a criminal to make the flight, and I'll even offer him his freedom if he does it."

Louis XVI had taken himself off the hook.

But among the spectators in the garden that day was a man named Pilatre de Rozier, a member of the King's court.

When Pilatre heard the King's pronouncement, he immediately stepped forward and asked to be heard.

"What is it, de Rozier?" asked the King.

"Your Majesty, such an honor as will be accorded the first man to journey in one of these airships should most certainly not go to a criminal. It belongs to a person more highly placed in society."

"And whom would you suggest?" the King asked.

"Let me go, Sire," said de Rozier.

At first Louis was doubtful. But de Rozier pleaded so ardently that eventually the King gave in. Pilatre de Rozier would be the first man to fly.

The brothers immediately began to construct another balloon, one large enough to carry a full-grown man. It took them less than a month.

On October 15, 1783, de Rozier walked without hesitation to the inflated balloon and climbed quickly into the gallery. There he found buckets of water and several sponges. These, the brothers told him, were to be used to extinguish any small fires ignited by sparks from the coals in the brazier beneath the balloon. This first manned flight was to be controlled by ropes, anchored to posts, which would remain attached to the balloon. They would be payed out from winches as the airship rose into the air.

At a signal from Joseph, the balloon was freed and the ropes began to unreel from the winches. A hush settled over the crowd. The King, who by now perhaps regretted his hesitancy over being the first man to fly, craned his neck as the balloon climbed.

The ship reached an altitude of 85 feet and strained at the ropes that held it back. Then de Rozier leaned over the side of the gallery and gaily waved a handkerchief. The crowd broke into wild applause.

In the balloon, Pilatre built a fire of straw in the brazier. He spent four hours aloft. Eventually he allowed the hot air in the balloon to cool and the taut lines began to slacken. Quickly the ship was pulled back to earth.

Before the first aviator had hardly stepped foot on the ground he was surrounded by a cheering, yelling crowd. They thronged around him and marveled at his bravery. Now, in this age of space capsules and supersonic airplanes,

Musée de l'Air, Paris

François Pilatre de Rozier (1754–1785)—Le premier homme qui ait quitté la terre—**the first man to leave the earth in an airship and, sadly enough, the first man to be killed by the new science.**

the feat of Pilatre de Rozier might seem insignificant. But remember that until his flight, no man in history had been able to rise off the earth. Many had tried and failed. No one knew what terrors the sky might hold, and those who were willing to risk the unknown were truly brave men.

Among those who marveled at Pilatre's exploit was the King, who by now was most assuredly sorry he had declined the honor Joseph Montgolfier had offered him.

"De Rozier," cried the King, "tell us! What was it like up there?"

"Wonderful!" exulted the first aviator. "Thrilling! There are hardly words to describe it. Twice sparks from the brazier caught the mouth of the ship afire and I had to move quickly to put them out. Thank heaven for those wet sponges."

"Tell us what you saw," yelled someone from the crowd. "What did we look like as you saw us from up there?"

"Like a multitude of two-legged ants," de Rozier laughed. "Everything seems to grow smaller. But it was beautiful! Absolutely beautiful."

As the crowd continued to plague de Rozier with questions, Joseph and Etienne inspected the balloon. They found it had been burned badly in several places.

"Joseph! Etienne!" cried de Rozier. "When shall you let me make another flight without being bound by the mooring lines? Today? Now, perhaps?"

"Patience," answered Etienne. "The burns must be repaired, and it would be better to make more captive flights. But soon you may make a free journey."

De Rozier did not press the issue. The brothers had accorded him a great honor. They obviously knew what they were doing.

He worked closely with Joseph and Etienne during the next few weeks and did make several more captive flights. But all were anxious for the next great step—the first free flight through space.

Finally, on November 21, 1783, the balloon was again inflated. This time the test was to be held in the gardens of the Chateau de la Muette. On hand to watch was a select group of spectators, again including Louis XVI and Marie Antoinette.

The original plan had called for Joseph Montgolfier to accompany de Rozier on this journey. But for a reason which history does not record, a French nobleman, the Marquis d'Arlandes, was selected instead.

The two adventurers stepped into the gallery and received the best wishes of the crowd. The word was given and the balloon shot straight up into the air as though it were a frisky colt just released from the halter it hated.

Later, in a letter to a friend, the Marquis described the emotions that swept over him as he realized he was completely free of the earth, that he was flying:

"We could do nothing for a few minutes but gape, our hearts beating with exultation, down at the earth. There, familiar objects had a new, strange, alluring aspect. Their very littleness, which was rapidly increasing, caused me to feel a contrawise, corresponding increase in my own stature and importance. . . . I considered myself the human lord of all below; that it was passing in review for my own especial pleasure and fawning pleasure in my eyes."

But the Marquis had little time to simply stand and be amazed at the view.

"We must attend the fire," de Rozier reminded him.

Members of the royal court of King Louis XVI gasped in wonder as the huge, beautifully decorated balloon built by the Montgolfier brothers leaped from its moorings at the start of man's first free flight through space.

They threw straw into the brazier to maintain the heat in the balloon and continued to drift in a gentle breeze. But the flight was not without its fearful moments.

"Look!" yelled de Rozier at one point. "We are descending and there is the river. Are we going to fall into it?"

Quickly they built up the heat and the balloon rose once again. All seemed to be going smoothly for a while when suddenly the Marquis felt the balloon shudder and jolt. He turned to look at de Rozier. "Are you dancing, sir?" he asked curiously.

"I did not stir," Pilatre answered indignantly.

They quickly examined the balloon and discovered that sparks from the brazier had ignited several small fires on the balloon's surface and that one of the ropes holding the gallery had burned through and snapped. Moving quickly, they applied wet sponges over the ship's surface as high as they could reach.

"Look," said de Rozier. "We are over Paris."

But the two men had little time to stand and stare at the famous jewel of Europe passing beneath them. The fire in the brazier had cooled somewhat, and before they could build it up the ship descended so low that it once scraped a chimney, knocking loose a few bricks. But they increased the heat and the balloon rose once again.

The ship passed completely over the city and out over the sprawling French countryside. There they allowed the fire to go out and the airship descended gracefully to earth.

The first balloon voyage and the first free flight through the sky by human beings were over. De Rozier and the Marquis stepped out of the gallery and received, with the determined Montgolfier brothers, the acclaim of the world.

Whether the Marquis flew again or not is unknown. De Rozier, however, was caught up in the adventure and continued making flights.

Musée de l'Air, Paris

Portrait of the Marquis d'Arlandes, de Rozier's courageous companion during the first free flight of an airship.

Sadly enough, he was killed two years later when attempting a balloon flight over the English Channel. The balloon crashed, killing Pilatre instantly. His companion, P. A. de Roman, died the next day. The first man to fly thus became the first aviator to be killed by the new science.

The Montgolfier brothers continued their work and their fame spread throughout the civilized world. It also stimulated other scientists to experiment with balloons. One of these was J. A. Charles, who used hydrogen gas instead of hot air to fill his balloon. This gas was more bouyant than hot air, and Charles' experiments made him almost as famous as the two paper makers.

Of what significance were these first balloon flights?

This question was best answered by Benjamin Franklin. He was in Paris as an envoy from the new nation across the sea, the nation which had just recently succeeded in gaining its freedom from England—the United States.

Franklin was watching one of Charles' hydrogen balloons soar upwards when a man next to him turned and asked in a skeptical voice, "What use is all this? Tell me. Of what use are these balloons?"

His eyes still on the soaring aircraft above him, Franklin replied, "Of what use is a newborn baby?"

"Have I Won?"

It was a fine day for kite flying. The brisk wind carried the kites high into the nearly cloudless sky. The group of boys was scattered around the field of rich green grass, laughing and yelling and running. They pulled and jerked the strings to make the multicolored kites dive and dodge above them.

"Hello. Hello, down there! Can you hear me?"

The voice, which came out of nowhere, startled all of the boys. They looked at each other in amazement, mixed with a little fright.

Then it came again, louder this time: "Hello! Can you hear me?"

The voice came from above. Was it an angel speaking from heaven?

Kites forgotten, the boys looked up and gaped in surprise.

Drifting toward them across the field was an airship shaped somewhat like a fat cigar with pointed ends. It floated lazily, less than seventy-five feet above the ground.

They saw the figure of a man standing in a basket suspended beneath the cigar-shaped bag. He waved his arms at them. "Can you hear me?" he yelled again.

They waved back. "Yes, yes," they shouted. "We can hear you."

The man pointed to a long rope which hung from the basket and trailed across the ground.

"Please," he yelled. "I am in trouble. See if you can grab the rope and try to stop me. Hurry!"

The boys quickly pulled down their kites. They raced across the field and grabbed the rope. The balloon slowed to a halt.

They began pulling it down and within minutes the basket touched the ground. The man leaped out, reached up and tore what seemed to be a patch from the skin of the bag. With a giant hiss the gas inside escaped and the bag began to collapse.

Speechless, the boys looked at the man. He was very small, weighing hardly more than a hundred pounds. He wore a large, neatly trimmed mustache. His clothes were in the highest kind of style for the year 1898.

He watched the bag collapse and appeared satisfied. Then he turned to the boys and smiled beneath the dark mustache. He removed his cap and bowed very graciously. "*Merci*, young gentlemen. You have saved me from what could have been a very embarrassing moment."

They were amazed. This stranger, whose voice they at first thought might belong to an angel, did not seem the slightest bit ruffled by the experience. In fact, he appeared to have enjoyed it.

They were still speechless as he put his hat back on, turned and began folding the balloon. He then put it into the basket and hoisted the whole package onto his back.

With another smile and nod to the boys, he walked across the field and was soon out of sight.

Balloons were not unusual sights around Paris, France, at the end of the nineteenth century. But it was indeed rare for one to drop out of nowhere into a field amidst a group of boys.

Quickly they gathered up their kites and ran to their homes. In excited voices they told their parents about the little man and how absolutely brave he must be to nearly crash and take it all so calmly.

The parents listened, nodded, and smiled or paid no attention at all, as parents sometimes do. The incident was soon forgotten, except perhaps by a few of the boys. In later years they may have heard a famous name and suddenly realized it belonged to the man who had interrupted their kite flying in so surprising a way.

The man was Albert Santos-Dumont. Within a short time after that day in the field, his name and his adventures were known in every Parisian household.

In the final years of the nineteenth century, aviation had not progressed much beyond the first experiments of the Montgolfier brothers. Many famous flights by many courageous men were made; yet the aircraft itself changed but little.

The death of de Rozier had marked the beginning of the end of the hot-air balloon. The brazier of coals was much too dangerous. Balloons filled with hydrogen and, later, helium gas, became popular.

But after more than a century the direction of flight still could not be controlled. Once in the air, the balloon was left to the whim of the wind. The pilot could do little more than control his rate of ascent by decreasing the weight of the basket. This was accomplished by carrying sandbags with the balloon. By emptying the sand overboard, the weight of

the ship was lightened, and the balloon rose higher. Speed of
descent was controlled by allowing some of the gas to escape
from the bag.

The next important step—controlling the flight—evaded
man for more than a century. Numerous methods were tried;
one of the strangest was a bicycle suspended from the bag.
The pilot pumped furiously to spin a small propeller. But
it was impossible to drive the propeller fast enough to over-
come the strength of the wind.

Steam engines and electric motors were tried, too. In some
cases the experiments partially succeeded. But these engines
were much too heavy for practical purposes.

Finally, in 1885, a German named Karl Benz constructed
an automobile powered by a gasoline engine. This type of
motor was light enough to be adapted to the balloon. But it
took thirteen years for someone to do it successfully.

And this someone was Albert Santos-Dumont.

When Albert began his experiments, the balloon had been
modified and somewhat improved over the first types invented by the Montgolfier brothers. An American, John
Wise, invented the ripping panel. This was a small patch
which could be torn from the skin of the bag. It allowed the
gas to escape quickly, preventing the balloon from being
dragged over the ground by strong winds.

Another important modification was the guide rope which
the boys in the field had grabbed to rescue Santos-Dumont.
It served several purposes. Dragging on the ground behind
the balloon, it helped control lift. At night, it warned the
pilot when the balloon passed over hills or water.

The guide rope also could cause considerable confusion
when it suddenly appeared out of nowhere and dragged
across the backs of horses pulling a plow through a French

farm field. And it also probably stimulated a few French housewives to voice unkind thoughts when it would drag across clotheslines from which hung freshly washed laundry.

Albert Santos-Dumont's native land was Brazil, South America. He was the son of a millionaire coffee plantation owner. Albert was eighteen years old when he first arrived in Paris, in 1891. He immediately fell in love with the city, over which Pilatre de Rozier and the Marquis d'Arlandes had made that first famous balloon flight more than a century before.

Ballooning had become something of a toy to most people. There were a few dedicated scientists who were always experimenting. Generally, though, people then accepted the sight of a balloon in the air as easily as people today accept jet airplanes passing overhead.

The thought of flying in a balloon intrigued Santos-Dumont. He had no idea that he might someday gain fame with the airships. He was very rich and gained a reputation as a playboy. He simply thought one day that ballooning might be an interesting adventure. More on impulse than anything else, he looked up a well-known Parisian balloonist and asked about the possibility of a short flight.

Albert's account of that first meeting is given in his book, *My Airships*:

> "You want to make an ascent?" he [the balloonist] asked gravely. "Hum! Hum! Are you sure you have the courage? A balloon ascent is no small thing and you seem so young."
>
> I assured him both of my purpose and my courage. Little by little he yielded to my arguments. Finally he consented to take me for a "short ascent." It must be on a calm, sunny afternoon, and not last for more than two hours.
>
> "My honorarium will be 1200 francs," he added. "And

you must sign me a contract to hold yourself responsible for all damages we may do to your own life and limbs and to mine, to the property of third parties, to the balloon and its accessories. Furthermore, you agree to pay our railroad fares and transportation for the balloon and its basket back to Paris from the point at which we come to ground."

I asked time for reflection. To a youth of eighteen years of age, 1200 francs was a large sum. How could I justify the spending of it to my parents. Then I reflected: "If I risk 1200 francs for an afternoon's pleasure, I shall find it either good or bad. If it is bad, the money will be lost. If it is good, I shall want to repeat it and I shall not have the means."

That decided me. Regretfully, I gave up ballooning and took refuge in automobiling.

And so, Albert bought an automobile, one of the first in Paris. He spent considerable time racing about the French countryside at the then incredible speed of 15 miles per hour. Eventually he returned to Brazil. But his curiosity about ballooning never left him.

One day he was browsing through a bookstore in Rio de Janeiro. He came across a book written by a Monsieur Lachambre, who had constructed the balloons and airships used to make some of the most famous flights of the nineteenth century. The old curiosity was rekindled as Albert read the book.

In 1898 he returned to Paris. One of his first acts was to look up Monsieur Lachambre.

"I am thinking of buying a balloon. But first I would like a demonstration," Albert told the Frenchman.

Lachambre agreed, and they made the flight.

This was all that was needed. The same feeling experienced by Pilatre de Rozier—and the one felt by modern men who love flying—swept over Albert. The sight of the farm fields and villages and woods and meadows and barking dogs passing below thrilled him beyond belief. It was so unreal, so beautiful!

He needed nothing more to convince him. From Lachambre he bought a tiny one-man balloon made of fine, strong

Albert Santos-Dumont, the dapper little balloonist who thrilled Paris with his exploits.

Japanese silk. In this small craft he bobbed around the French countryside until he had mastered the art of balloon flight. Then he bought a larger craft and made longer flights.

Although he enjoyed the sport tremendously, the long trips by train or wagon back to his home annoyed him. He wanted both to go and to return by air. But as long as the wind controlled the direction of flight, this was impossible.

Albert began to study all that had been written about dirigibles—balloons powered by engines. He decided that the gasoline powered engines were the only type light enough and strong enough to do the job. But he could not find any that were suitable.

Despite his reputation as a millionaire playboy, Albert was a very self-disciplined man. He possessed a bright intelligence and knew the value of logic in solving a problem. Although he is not reported to have uttered the words, his philosophy of life may well have been: "What is logical is possible. What is possible, I can do."

Since there were no suitable engines available, he decided that he would build one. He removed the engine from his automobile and rebuilt it to lighten its weight. Then he added a shaft for a large, two-bladed, silk-covered propeller, which he also built.

Albert even devised an ingenious way of testing his engine by hanging it with ropes from a beam in his workshop. The engine had a pull of 25 pounds, which Albert calculated was enough to move his ship through the air at about 20 miles per hour.

As he tested and experimented, Albert grew more excited. He knew he would succeed. He did not doubt it. Everything was done in a precise, logical way.

The next step was to design a very different type of bag.

Instead of its being round, he made it cigar-shaped and pointed at both ends. Unlike other balloons, this one did not have an opening at the bottom from which the gas could escape.

Albert installed a pressure valve that released the gas before the bag reached the bursting point. This was a necessary safety factor. As a balloon rises, the gas inside will expand as the atmospheric pressure decreases at high altitudes. If not allowed to escape, the gas would expand so much that the bag would burst. Albert also installed an air pressure pump into the aircraft. If the bag would for some reason begin to collapse during the flight, he would be able to pump enough air into it to allow him to come down to earth gently.

To control ascent and descent he hung two sandbags on ropes that stretched from the basket to the nose and tail of the dirigible. When he wished to go up, he would pull the front bag back to him. With most of the weight in the back, the tail would dip and the engine would then push upwards. With the rear bag moved forward, the front would dip and the ship would go down. To make turns Albert installed a rudder which operated on the same principles as those on modern airplanes.

Finally the day came. The *Santos-Dumont I* was ready to fly.

And so, thought Albert, there it is. It is complete. There is nothing left to do but fly it. By this time in his experiments he had trained several assistants. With their help he carried the *Santos-Dumont I* to a field. It did not take very long to fill the bag with gas, but Albert felt the minutes were passing as hours.

Then it was ready. Impatient to begin, he stepped into the basket and told his assistants to start the engine. It came to life quickly. The silk-covered propeller spun in front of the basket. The dirigible moved gently until it tugged against the restraining lines. Quickly, Albert pulled the front sandbag back to the basket. The nose of the dirigible lifted.

Perfect, he thought. It's going to work. He signaled his assistants to gradually pay out the ropes.

Then—disaster!

His men misunderstood his signal. They suddenly released the lines instead of feeding them out gradually.

Albert was thrown off balance as the ship lurched into the wind. Before he could do anything, the wind threw the ship into some nearby trees. It fell the few feet to the ground where it lay ripped and torn as the gas escaped.

The horrified assistants ran to the tangle of rope, basket and bag.

Albert crawled from the basket and turned to survey the damage. His assistants waited.

"Well, gentlemen," Albert announced, "it appears we have suffered an unfortunate incident. I do not think it will take much to repair the damage. Gather up everything and carry it to the shop. We shall repair what needs repairing and try again."

The damage was not extensive and the repairs were made in a few days. Once again the ship was carried to the field, filled with gas and made ready.

The tension was even greater than it had been on the previous test. Would anything go wrong today?

The engine sputtered into action. Albert lifted the ship's nose and gave the signal. The assistants payed out the ropes slowly. Gently, the ship lifted. Albert untied the restraining ropes and threw them to the ground.

In a few minutes, the familiar French countryside passed below.

It worked! Everything worked! He flew the *No. 1* into the wind, with the wind, and to the side of the wind. The little ship responded to every touch.

Everything worked.

But of course it did, he thought. After all, had not everything been done in a perfectly logical way?

The flight continued as he experimented for a while longer. Then he settled back into the basket, steering the ship along. It was a bright warm day, a beautiful day. Only a few clouds floated lazily in the sky. It was a wonderful day to be alive.

The trip continued for a short time longer. Then the countryside below darkened as one of the clouds passed beneath the sun. It was a large cloud and hid the warmth for several minutes.

The ship lurched suddenly. Startled, Albert looked up. The dirigible sagged in its center. The gas inside the bag began to cool when the cloud hid the sun. The gas was contracting!

The pressure pump!

Quickly Albert began to push the air pump's handle back and forth. But something was wrong. It was not working. He tried a few minutes more, but to no avail. The pump was useless.

The flight became dangerous. The bag could not be controlled because it sagged in the center. Albert threw out the guide rope, hoping it would catch in a bush or wrap itself around a tree trunk. But it did not.

Then ahead of him he saw the field where the boys were

flying their kites. With a great sigh of relief, he called to them. He saw surprise on their faces as they looked upward to the "angel."

After they had rescued him, he returned home. His assistants gathered around with a hundred questions. As they listened in astonishment, he reported on the flight.

After describing how the boys had saved him, he said: "And now, gentlemen, back to work. The air pump must be put in order in case a similar mishap should occur.

"And, if you will pardon me, I shall go and bathe and change into fresh clothes. The trip home was very dusty. It also has raised my appetite. I wonder what the cook has prepared for my meal."

He walked into the house to find out.

During the next few years Albert continued with his experiments. He built twelve different dirigibles, calling them *No. 1, No. 2,* and so on. This, of course, was the simple, logical way of doing it.

The sight of the dapper little man sailing over Paris became commonplace. The city's people soon developed a strong affection for the jaunty Brazilian. They delighted in exchanging variations of stories, some of them quite impossible (or were they?) of his adventures.

Not all his flights were smooth, however. He developed a great fondness for large trees whose broad limbs absorbed the shock of landing when something went wrong and the ship crashed. More than once he made his way home bruised and scratched from one of his "unfortunate incidents."

He often delighted and amused the people of Paris by bringing his ship down to street level next to a sidewalk café. He would order a light meal and remain in his basket while he ate. Then, with a flourish, he would speed up the propeller and lift into the sky. Below him, young children, laughing and yelling, ran after the ship until it was out of sight.

More than once the servants in his home would unexpectedly hear him calling from outside. They ran out and helped tie down the dirigible. Then their master would enter the house, wash, eat a light meal, return to the aircraft and take off again.

Paris loved Santos-Dumont. He in turn loved the city and its people. He was a generous man. The improvements and designs he made for the dirigible were patentable. He could easily not have allowed them to be used by other aviators. But this was not his way, and he gave his ideas away freely.

Just as he loved life, and just as he believed that a man had a right to be an individual, so did Albert believe in the future of aviation. He knew that flight was a new frontier to mankind. He knew the science needed to grow. But it could not unless public interest stimulated it.

Despite the fact that he was well known and that his exploits were famous, he longed for one great accomplishment. It had to be something startling, something unheard-of—something that would focus the eyes of the world on flight.

His opportunity finally came in 1900 when a prize was offered for the first person to fly from Paris's Aero Park Club to and around the Eiffel Tower and back to the club. This was the chance Albert had been waiting for. The trip had to be made in half an hour. This was considered to be next to impossible, since the total distance round-trip was seven miles.

Albert immediately began construction of his *No. 5.* By July 13, 1901, it was completed and he attempted to make the trip. All went well until he rounded the tower and began the return trip.

Suddenly the motor sputtered, popped once or twice and quit. The wind caught the ship and threw it into the friendly treetops. Luckily, neither ship nor pilot was hurt.

Less than a month later he made another try, and once again he rounded the tower and began the trip back.

The wind was heavy and the ship beat its way through the air. Then one of the suspension ropes holding the basket snapped and fouled the propeller. Quickly Albert turned the engine off and the dirigible was once again left to the mercy of the wind. The ship drifted over Paris and finally crashed into the top of a hotel.

Firemen rescued Albert, who escaped the crash entirely unhurt. It was but another "unfortunate incident."

Far from discouraged, the little Brazilian immediately began construction of *No. 6*. It was larger than any of the others and carried a 16-horsepower engine.

Finally, on October 19, it was ready, and once again Albert prepared for the contest against time.

The weather on the day before had been wretched, and had improved little by mid-afternoon of the nineteenth. A strong wind chilled the bleak fall afternoon. But Albert was determined, and shrugged aside the advice of friends who urged him to put the contest off until another day.

At 2:42 P.M. the ship lifted into the air. It rose to a height of about 800 feet. The wind was astern of the ship, and the trip to and around the tower took only nine minutes.

Then the return flight began. Now the ship was once again beating into the wind.

Albert was optimistic. He had 21 minutes remaining of the allotted half hour. This time he would make it!

A huge crowd had gathered along the path of the flight and was watching in eager anticipation. They applauded loudly as the ship passed overhead.

Santos-Dumont's No. 16 dirigible, which was basically the same as the No. 6 in which he made his famous flight around the Eiffel Tower.

The tower was well behind him when Albert sucked in his breath sharply. Something was wrong with the motor. It had begun to lose speed.

He was faced with a hard decision that must be made quickly: quit or try to fix the trouble. He knew that to reach the engine he would have to release the rudder and risk drifting off his course. And ahead of him he could see the finishing point. It was so close.

The engine continued to lose speed and was nearly at the point of stopping completely. Albert sighed. Well, he thought, I will repair it and try again. Tomorrow, perhaps, I can . . .

The engine popped again and then, miraculously, it began to pick up speed once more. The ship surged ahead. All was not yet lost.

Several times more the motor lost and then regained speed. And finally the ship reached the club and neared the finishing line. The crowd began to applaud. Its cheers turned into cries of alarm as the engine suddenly slowed again, and just as quickly surged to full speed. The ship seemed to pitch itself into a dangerously vertical angle. Then it righted itself.

The sudden jerk startled Albert, but it did not alarm him. A quick glance down told him he was over his old friends, the treetops, whose soft greenery always reassured him.

He looked down. The airship was pushing along at full speed now.

Then it was over. The finishing line passed beneath. Albert turned the ship and flew low over the crowd. Several men grabbed his guide rope and pulled the ship down.

Albert had timed himself, and he knew the race was close.

But he did not know the exact minutes the trip had taken.

As the basket neared the ground he leaned out and cried, "Have I won?"

"Yes," the crowd yelled back to him. "Yes!"

He had made the trip in 29 minutes and 31 seconds.

He had indeed won, and within a short time the entire civilized world knew it.

Part II

The Birdmen

The Montgolfier brothers and Santos-Dumont were only three of hundreds of men captured by the dream of flight. During the eighteenth and nineteenth centuries, thousands of balloon flights were made by daring men of vision. Their adventures caught the admiring attention of the world.

The development of the dirigible marked the final phase of the history of the balloon. These gigantic airships became a popular means of air transportation. They could carry passengers great distances, even across oceans.

On May 3, 1937, a tragic accident climaxed the story of the dirigible. On that day a giant airship named the *Hindenburg* exploded while landing at Lakehurst, New Jersey, at the end of a transoceanic trip from Germany. Thirty-six of the 97 passengers aboard were killed and many more were horribly burned. This tragedy brought the era of the balloon to its end. Although dirigibles still are occasionally seen in the skies, their use has become very limited.

But even during the nineteenth century, many believed the balloon was not the final answer to man's desire for equality with the birds. They believed the true future of aviation lay in flight with winged aircraft, not with bulky, gas-filled bags.

Balloons flew because the gas inside them was lighter than the air. But birds are heavier than air, reasoned the men of the sky, and *they* fly.

How?

That was the question. How?

Is it not possible, they asked themselves, for man to construct a machine that would duplicate birds' flight?

Yes, they answered. It *is* possible. Birds fly by laws of nature. Discover those laws and man can imitate bird flight.

During the eighteenth and nineteenth centuries many men pursued this dream. Some sought it foolishly. The wiser ones looked for it scientifically.

The man who is credited with laying the groundwork for the future of heavier-than-air flight is Sir George Cayley of England. Even as a child, he was fascinated by the dream of flight, as were almost all the aviation pioneers. As the years passed he studied the science of flight and made numerous experiments with different types of model aircraft. Finally, in 1810, he published a report on his research. This work and his later discoveries earned Sir George the title, "Father of Aviation."

During the nineteenth century hundreds of other men from all parts of the civilized world pursued the dream of flight. Some of their ideas worked a little, some not at all. As with the development of the dirigible, suitable power was a major problem. The steam and electric engines of that era were not practical because they were too heavy.

Many of the early experimenters turned their attention to the motorless glider, an aircraft that stays aloft by floating on the currents of air that rise from the earth's surface. If man could design gliders which flew and which could be controlled in the air, he would begin to master the great dream. The next logical step—putting an engine on the glider—could come later.

There were many discoveries about flight during the nineteenth century. But they were random discoveries. All but a few of the experimenters failed to realize or overlooked one very important requirement—for an experiment to be successful, the laws of nature which make it a success must be researched, analyzed, studied and applied.

It is not enough to build a glider which has wings and which may or may not fly. Why does or doesn't it fly? What laws of nature lie behind the phenomenon? How are these laws applied?

The question is always, "Why?"

When we know the answer, thought the men of the sky, we will master the dream.

Many men sought the answer scientifically. The most outstanding of these—one who pursued the great dream for almost all of his lifetime—has been called "the Father of Gliding."

His name was Otto Lilienthal.

The Last Flight

"MEIN HERR, perhaps we should wait until tomorrow," said the servant. There was worry in his voice. His eyes searched the sky. Black, ominous clouds rolled and churned across the heavens high above.

The servant and his master, Otto Lilienthal, were standing at the top of a small hill. The slopes of the hill were smooth and even on all sides.

"Don't worry," said Otto. "This will be the last flight today. I think if I take a grip a little further forward, my balance will be perfect."

The servant watched as his master positioned himself in the center of a strange-looking contraption that resembled the curved wings of a bird. A short tail projected behind the center of the aircraft. The machine was a glider that Otto had designed and built.

A wooden frame hung beneath the center of the glider's wing. Otto lifted the lightweight aircraft over his head and gripped the wooden frame tightly. A sudden gust of wind suddenly slapped the top of the hill and nearly lifted one

49

side of the glider into the air. Otto took a firmer grip and spread his feet. He was a heavy man and very strong.

The servant had seen the wind lift the glider. "Please, *mein herr*," he pleaded, "we can wait one more day. Let's finish these tests tomorrow."

Otto smiled gently. "No, we must finish today. We are so *close*. We have almost all the answers."

The servant sighed. It would be no use. When *Herr* Lilienthal made up his mind to do something, no one could persuade him not to do it.

"All right," he said. "I'll go to the bottom of the hill and wait for you. But please, be careful!"

"I will. Don't worry."

The servant started toward the bottom of the hill—the "cone," Otto called it. It was huge mound of earth that Otto and his brother, Gustav, had built—a small man-made mountain fifty feet high and located near Berlin, Germany. Built into its man-made peak was a small building for storing the Lilienthal gliders.

Otto was right, the servant said to himself. They were so close to the answer. But the danger was always present. Otto had already survived a bad crash. The glider had dropped from an altitude of sixty feet and crashed into a meadow. Miraculously, Otto suffered only a flesh wound on the side of his head and a sprained arm.

It had not been the first accident, nor was it likely to be the last. We are challenging an unknown enemy, and we are not yet fully armored for battle, thought the servant.

He reached the bottom of the hill and took his position as observer.

At the hill's peak, Otto made the necessary last-minute

adjustments. He should be ready to take off in a few more minutes. He would run down the side of the hill into the wind until he gained enough speed for the wind to lift the wings of the glider from the ground.

Then he would soar several hundred feet at a height of perhaps forty or fifty feet. The flight would last only a few seconds.

It is strange, thought Otto. We have been testing our gliders for more than five years. We have made more than two thousand flights. Yet if we add all the minutes of actual flight in these tests, the total is hardly more than five hours. Five hours out of two thousand flights. It seems so little. But we have done so much and the end is so near. In a few days our dream will become reality.

Otto sighed. The dream, the great dream. It had begun for himself and his brother, Gustav, long ago. The brothers' man-made hill near Berlin was separated by both time and miles from the small village of Anclam, Pomerania, in Prussia, where Otto and Gustav were born.

In the meadows around Anclam, large flocks of pelicans nested and bore their young. Even as a boy, Otto had been fascinated by the birds. On the ground the huge, ungainly creatures waddled pompously about, preening themselves with their long beaks.

But in the air their clumsiness vanished and they became beautiful to behold. They were pure grace as they moved their wings in a steady rhythmic motion or as they extended their wings and dipped and banked over and through air currents.

How do they fly, Otto would ask himself. How?

The idea of flight possessed Otto and he began to follow

the great dream. He began reading everything available about the science, including the theories put forth by Sir George Cayley.

One day, not too long after his thirteenth birthday, Otto and Gustav stationed themselves in a clump of trees near a meadow. From there they could study the movements of the pelicans without being seen. They lay for an hour, not moving, speaking only in whispers.

Near the edge of the flock, two birds caught Otto's particular interest—a mother pelican and her youngster. The mother would stand beside her offspring for a moment and then begin to run and flap her wings. Then she would stop and return to her child and do the same thing over again.

Time and time again she repeated this strange behavior. At first the young pelican did nothing but watch.

Then, to Otto's surprise, the younger bird began to run beside its mother and to flap its wings as she did. Over and over again the two birds repeated this peculiar ritual. Finally the smaller bird actually began to leave the ground for very short periods of time. But as the practice continued, it stayed aloft for longer periods.

Otto suddenly realized what was happening.

"Gustav," he said in an excited voice, "the pelicans are not born with the knowledge of flight. They must be taught how to soar. That is what the mother pelican is doing. She is teaching him how to fly!"

Gustav, who was only about eight years old at the time, might not have understood the full implication of Otto's discovery. But he knew it was something important because his older brother began to make notes furiously.

"And even when the young bird understood what its

mother was trying to do, it still could not fly," Otto said. "It had to keep trying over and over again.

"It had to practice!"

And so, on this fine sunny day, Otto Lilienthal learned two important lessons. They were to influence his whole thinking process and were to lead to the discoveries that laid a solid foundation for the world of flight.

"Like the small pelican, man must study flight to master it," Otto went on. "Once he understands the principles of flight, man must practice—over and over again—what he has learned."

So excited was Otto over his discovery that he stood up suddenly, frightening the flock of pelicans he and Gustav had been watching. Immediately the huge birds stirred and began to hop, trying to fly away.

How peculiar, thought Otto. They are frightened and are trying to escape. Yet they are running directly at me, not away from me, even though they see me standing here. Why aren't they running in the opposite direction?

He then became aware of the cool breeze on the back of his neck as he faced the birds. The answer came to him.

"Of course! They are running into the wind. That must mean it is easier for them to fly against the wind than with it. They are using the weight of the wind to help lift themselves into the air."

Excited over what they had discovered, the two boys returned home. They begged a large quantity of cloth from their mother, but did not tell her what they wanted it for. After all, Frau Lilienthal was a mother; and even now, more than a century later, what mother would relish the idea of her teenage son building a machine that would let him fly?

The two boys spent the next few days building "flying machines." The first one had wings that measured six feet long and three feet wide. Then they built another, measuring nine by three feet. But their tests with these models failed, and sadly they dismantled them.

Although they had not been able to achieve flight, the boys were not discouraged. They continued observing the birds and studying all the information they could find on the science of aviation.

As the years passed, Otto's interest in flight never left him. He continued his studies and made experiments with model gliders. At the Berlin Trade School he studied engineering. Here he learned the value of the scientific approach to a problem.

In 1870 he served with the German military services during the Franco-Prussian War. When Germany won in 1871, Otto returned home. His thirst for knowledge led him along many paths. He invented types of boilers, and pulleys and sirens. Eventually he established a business to manufacture these things.

But the call of the great dream remained loud in his mind and, already successful as an inventor and engineer, he began to concentrate most of his efforts on flight. Gustav, who always was satisfied to remain in the background as a follower and reporter, worked with his brother.

From the early 1870's to 1891 Otto applied himself to the study of aerodynamic principles—the laws of nature which govern flight. Like a few other aviation scientists, Otto realized that curved or "cambered" wings were far superior than flat wings for successful flight. He studied this principle until he was satisfied it was the only answer to proper wing shape.

Finally, in 1891, he decided that he had come as far as he could with his calculations and theories. The next step was to put them to the test. He and Gustav began to build a series of gliders and for the next five years devoted most of their time to the experiments.

Thus, Otto was putting to use the discovery he had made by the meadow so many years before. Like the baby pelican, he had studied until he understood. Then he began to practice what he had learned.

"Man," Otto wrote, "must serve an apprenticeship to the birds."

Otto's first gliders were monoplanes (one wing) with cambered wings and a tail. During the flights, Otto would dangle from a small framework built at the center point of the wing. To control the flight he would swing his legs or shift his weight in order to keep the wings level.

News of Otto's experiments spread, and photographs of his flights were sent around the world. These pictures stimulated the world's admiration for this methodical, somewhat stubborn, but tremendously courageous German.

Once in position in his aircraft, Otto would run down the slope of a hill and into the wind. When he had gained enough speed he lifted his legs from the ground and swept forward in gliding flight. His speed was fast enough to carry him through the air. The wings of the glider were large enough to carry his weight. Thus, he flew.

Sometimes the flight might last a full minute. More often it lasted only seconds.

As he flew, Otto taught himself how to move his legs and shift his body to maintain even flight. Proper balance is instinctive in the human being when he walks on the ground. But put him on a high wire and he must train that balance.

Otto Lilienthal prepares for a glider flight from the top of the 50-foot-high hill he and his brother, Gustav, built near Berlin, Germany.

Otto runs into the wind until his speed is fast enough for the breeze to lift the glider into the air. It was during such a flight that the courageous aviator fell to his death in 1896.

Otto controlled the direction of his flight by shifting his weight from one side of the glider frame to the other.

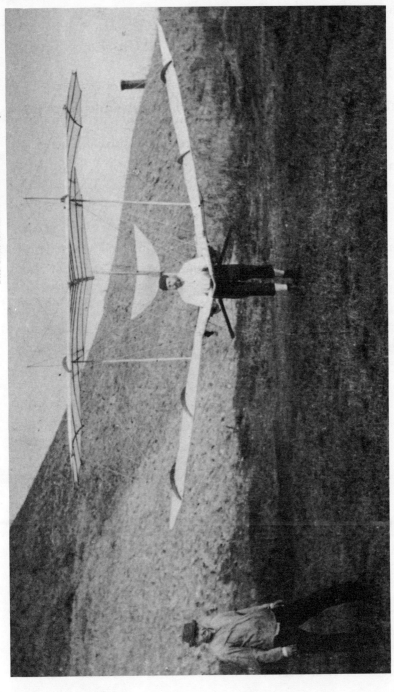

The flight over, Otto poses with a friend. Although Otto made more than 2,000 glider flights, his total time in the air was hardly more than five hours. Yet his experiments helped lay the groundwork for modern aviation.

He must tune it like a fine piano. And Otto tuned his sense of balance to its finest pitch.

One of his most troublesome problems was a proper location for his experiments. His experiments called for him to run down a slope into the wind. But often he could not find a hill facing the direction from which the wind blew. In 1893 he moved his experiments to the Rhinow Mountains where there was a range of gradually sloping hills that seemed just right for his work.

It was here that he met with the accident that sprained his arm and gave him the flesh wound on the side of the head.

He had been moving through the air at a speed of about 35 miles an hour at about a height of sixty feet. Suddenly the aircraft was shot upward by a sudden gust of wind. Then it turned and dived downward. Otto fought to regain balance, but it was useless. Describing the accident in his book, *Birdflight as the Basis of Aviation*, Otto wrote:

> The machine rushed with me vertically towards the earth. With my senses quite clear . . . and still holding the apparatus firmly with my hands, I fell towards a greensward [meadow]; a shock, a crash, and I lay with the apparatus on the ground.

The accident, which might have unnerved other men, only served to remind Otto of the need for a superior sense of balance. It did not take him long to recuperate, and at the first opportunity he took to the air once more.

Long hours of theorizing, testing, studying and more testing continued. In 1894, the year following the near-fatal accident, Otto and Gustav built the 50-foot-high hill at Gross-Licthfelde, near Berlin. It sloped in all directions, so Otto need not worry about proper wind direction. No matter where the wind came from, he could run down the hill into it.

The problem of stability was always on Otto's mind. He wished to make longer flights, to remain aloft minutes instead of mere seconds. He began experimenting with different types of wing structures and finally decided that the bi-plane glider (two wings) might be the answer. He built several models and they seemed to prove his theory.

But again, a theory, to have practical value, must be proven. This belief was one of Otto Lilienthal's most outstanding characteristics. And there was but one way to prove a theory: test it. It took courage to test a theory which, if wrong, could mean his death. He showed this personal courage when he wrote:

"Actual trial alone can decide this matter, as we must let the air and the wind have their say in the matter."

Otto built his bi-plane glider and found it could accomplish much better glides than his previous, one-winged machines. At times he would reach an altitude higher than his original starting point. Occasionally, he could hover motionless in the air.

Early in his experiments Otto set aside ideas of putting an engine onto the airplane. He decided that power was not the first problem. We must master the science of flight first, he thought. Later we shall add the power.

By 1896 Otto was ready to think about powered flight. He also wanted to experiment with movable wing and tail surfaces. Until then they had been solid, and flight was controlled by only the pilot's body movements. With movable surfaces, the stability of the machine in the air could be controlled even better than by Otto's finely-tuned sense of balance.

The next great step was at hand.

Otto and Gustav constructed a simple engine. Its purpose, however, was not to drive a propeller. It was to move the wings of the aircraft up and down, in imitation of bird flight.

Otto also developed a rudder for the aircraft. It was an idea that was new and, of course, it must be tested. If it worked it would be put on the engine-driven machine. The rudder operated by a rope or line attached to a belt around Otto's forehead. Thus he could control its movement by a motion of his head. If it worked well, the experiment with the engine-driven aircraft could be held in the near future.

This was the device that Otto wanted to test on that blustery, windy August 9, 1896.

The servant waited at the bottom of the hill.

"Are you ready?" Otto called from the top of the hill.

The servant waved his arm. "Ready!" he yelled back.

The wind blew in gusts behind him, but he tried to conceal the worry in his voice. "Ready!" he yelled again.

Otto made a final adjustment to the band around his neck.

With another wave, Otto began to run down the slope, faster and faster.

He raised his feet from the ground and the glider lifted. It rose higher and higher into the air until it was nearly even with the top of the hill.

The servant watched, and breathed a little easier. It seemed to be going well.

Wait!

A strong gust of the unruly wind pitched the glider up and then down again. He could see Otto's feet swinging as he fought to regain balance.

Another gust and the aircraft pitched suddenly downward. It dove straight into the earth and demolished itself.

Filled with horror, the servant ran to the wreck.

"*Herr* Lilienthal!"

There was no answer.

Several people who had seen the accident ran to the scene. They found the servant kneeling beside his master's still form. The servant looked up at them, his eyes brimming with tears.

"He is hurt. He is hurt, badly. Please get help. Please."

Carefully they carried the unconscious aviator to a nearby shelter. A doctor came and examined Otto.

"There is nothing we can do," he said. "His back is broken."

The next day, without regaining consciousness, Otto Lilienthal died. The last flight was over.

Kitty Hawk

"I HAVE A PRESENT for you boys."

The two brothers, Orville and Wilbur, crowded around their father. He held his hands cupped together in front of him. Their mother, their two older brothers, and their baby sister, Kate, watched.

"It's called a helicopter. It's a flying machine," Reverend Milton Wright said. "Watch." He opened his hands and with a sudden whirr, a little machine jumped from his hands. It leaped to the ceiling and bumped its way around for several moments. The boys stared in delighted amazement.

The toy's curiously shaped wings were powered by rubber bands and were spinning furiously. Then they began to slow down. The little machine floated slowly toward the floor. Reverend Wright caught it.

"Here," he said, handing it to Wilbur. "Take it outside. Inside the house is no place for a toy like this."

Wilbur, who was eleven years old, took the little machine. "Thank you, Father." His eyes were shining with excitement. "C'mon, Orville. Let's see how high it can go."

The two boys ran from the house. As the door closed behind them, Mr. Wright turned to his wife. "Those two are
really a pair, aren't they? Did you see how excited they
were?"

Mrs. Wright nodded.

"I'm very proud of them," Mr. Wright added. "They
have wonderful minds and they know how to use them."

Mrs. Wright laughed. "That they surely do. And they've
got more than their share of curiosity, too. I'd hate to try to
count how many times one or the other of them asks 'why'
and 'how' during one day."

"All boys are like that," her husband said, laughing with
his wife. "It's a good sign. And if I know Wilbur and Orville, it won't be long before they know just how that little
helicopter works."

"Yes, they probably will. I've never seen two boys who had
to have answers as much as they do."

She paused and sobered a little bit. "Sometimes I wonder
what will happen to them. Maybe all that curiosity will get
them into trouble when they grow up."

"Now, Mother," Mr. Wright said gently. "If what Wilbur
and Orville are like right now is any sign of what they'll be
as grown-ups, you don't have anything to worry about.
They're going to leave a real sizable mark on the world."

He walked to the window and looked out into the yard.
The two brothers were crouched on the ground, their new
toy between them. Wilbur was winding the propeller-like
wings.

With a yell they jumped up and watched the little machine
soar straight up, forty or fifty feet over their heads. It came
back to the ground and they ran to retrieve it.

"Yes," said Mr. Wright to himself. "A real sizable mark."

The year that the two brothers received the toy helicopter from their father was 1878. A quarter of a century later, on December 17, 1903, Mr. Wright received the following telegram:

SUCCESS. FOUR FLIGHTS THURSDAY MORNING. ALL AGAINST TWENTY-ONE MILE WIND. STARTED FROM LEVEL WITH ENGINE POWER ALONE. AVERAGE SPEED THROUGH AIR THIRTY-ONE MILES. LONGEST 57 SECONDS. INFORM PRESS. HOME CHRISTMAS.

ORVELLE WRIGHT

The telegraph operator had misspelled Orville's name. That error was unimportant to those who understood what the telegram meant.

The great dream had become a reality.

Wilbur and Orville Wright succeeded where hundreds of other men failed. They had flown in an aircraft that *pulled itself* off the ground and into the air.

They had conquered the dream. Now man was master of both earth and sky.

The simple, straightforward message that Mr. Wright received that winter day so many years ago could not tell the whole story. At that time, only the Wright brothers' friends and relatives knew about the years of tests, of failures and more tests that led up to the telegram. But the story of those years is one of determination and of personal courage.

On the surface, it is a simple story. But simple stories can become legends. And the Wright brothers are indeed legendary.

Wilbur Wright was born on April 16, 1867, near Newcastle, Indiana. A few years later his father, who became a Bishop of the United Brethren Church, moved his family to Dayton, Ohio. There, Orville was born on August 19, 1871.

The members of the Wright family were very close to each other. All the children were taught very early in life that patience and painstaking care were the most valuable of virtues. From their father the children learned the true meaning of integrity and honesty. These traits, added to their highly developed curiosity and their personal courage, eventually helped them achieve the magnificent goal.

But 1903 seemed centuries away to the two boys playing with their new toy in the front yard of their Dayton home.

And, as their father predicted, they had, indeed, soon taken the little helicopter apart. Later they built similar models. The memory of the pleasure they received from the toy never left the brothers. Many years later they wrote: "A toy so delicate lasted but a short time in the hands of small boys, but its memory was abiding."

The years passed and the two brothers grew into young men. As a minister, their father did not receive a great deal of money in those days, and eventually the boys had to start earning money. Together they started a small newspaper and then worked a short while as printers. Both were very mechanically minded. They also spent much of their spare time reading. And as they read, they learned.

They soon developed a new design for a bicycle. It was successful, and the brothers established a bicycle repair and manufacturing business in Dayton.

The business grew rapidly. All who knew the brothers considered them good businessmen of honesty and integrity.

The brothers' interest in science was always strong. The memory of that toy helicopter in their childhood still lingered. They avidly read all that they found on the new science of aviation. The work of the famous German aviator, Otto Lilienthal, caught their particular interest.

On a warm August day in 1896, Orville heard Wilbur calling from the door of their shop. He looked up to see his brother approaching with a newspaper in his hand.

"Look," said Wilbur. "This is sad news. He was a great man."

A brief item in the paper reported the tragic death of Lilienthal.

"He just might have succeeded," Wilbur mused. "Just think how much he has accomplished in five years. If he could have kept going, perhaps he might have shown us how to fly."

Later, at home, Wilbur was browsing through his library. A particular book caught his attention. It was titled *Animal Mechanism* and was a study of how birds fly. Wilbur already had read the book several times. Now, with Lilienthal's accomplishments on his mind, he re-read the volume. The book greatly stimulated Wilbur's interest. In the next few weeks he obtained more modern books on the science of flight. Typically, he mentioned it to his brother, and Orville, too, began studying the subject.

Soon the science of aviation was practically all they could think about. Already familiar with Lilienthal's work, they concentrated heavily on reports the German had written on his experiments.

Shortly before his death, Lilienthal had published a book summing up the results of his experiments. The brothers decided this report would be valuable to their studies. They ordered it from a publisher in Germany. When it arrived, they were amazed to discover that it was printed in the German language.

"We should have known it would be," laughed Orville.

"Well," sighed Wilbur, "I suppose there's only one thing we can do."

"Yes," replied Orville. "I guess we'll just have to learn how to read German. What else is there to do?"

Wilbur nodded. "You're right."

And they did.

Before very long the brothers were completely submerged in aviation science. And as they studied the work of other aviation pioneers, particularly Lilienthal, they began to draw their own conclusions about flight.

They agreed that the most difficult part of flying was balance. Lilienthal had kept his gliders in the air by shifting the weight of his body from side to side whenever the wings of his aircraft began to tilt.

There must be a way, the brothers decided, to control the balance of a glider mechanically instead of by shifting the pilot's weight.

They did not know the answer, but they did know how to find it: tests and experiments, and then more tests and experiments until they had the answer.

Most of the early glider pioneers had been wrong in their approach to the problem. They believed that a properly designed glider would have a natural stability that would keep the wings level when they were tipped up or down by gusts of wind. The Wright brothers' experiments led them to conclude that this approach was wrong. But *how* was it wrong?

After long months of study, Orville finally found the answer.

"And it's so simple," he exclaimed to Wilbur. "Maybe that's why no one has thought of it before. Everyone has been looking too high for the answer when all the time it's been staring them in the face.

"We know that if you tilt the front of a wing up, the wind will hit the bottom of the wing and lift it up. What we have to do is design a wing that the pilot can twist whenever the glider begins to tip over. If the left wing begins to drop in the wind, all the pilot has to do is twist the tip up for a moment and the glider will regain its balance."

"That's it," exclaimed Wilbur. "You've got it!"

"You mean we've got the theory," said Orville. "Now we have to learn how to put it to work."

For the next several months that was the major problem they concentrated upon—how can the wing tips be twisted? They tried several systems, none of which worked well. Orville designed one mechanism that seemed to be the answer, but it was much too heavy for the frame of the glider.

One day a customer entered the bicycle shop and purchased an inner tube. While chatting with the customer, Wilbur was idly toying with the cardboard box that had held the inner tube.

Suddenly he looked at the boxtop he held in his hands. He had bent the box so that one end was twisted downward and the other upward.

The answer!

Immediately he realized that the wing of a glider could easily be twisted or "warped" by a simple system of wires leading from the wing tips to the pilot. If a wing began to dip in the wind, all the pilot had to do was pull the wire leading to the tip, causing it to bend downward. The flow of the wind would catch the "warped" edge of the tip and raise it.

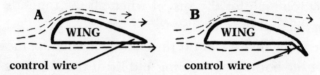

Warping. In level flight (A) air flows past the wings evenly. If either wing begins to drop, pilot pulls its control wire to bend the rear edge of the wing (B). Force of air against the warped edge pushes wing up.

Immediately Wilbur called his brother and explained the idea. They agreed this idea was the one they had been searching for.

Up to this point, the Wright brothers had spent most of their time studying the concepts of flight and had done very little actual experimenting.

But now they had discovered the means of achieving balance in flight—the concept of "warping" the wing tips. The time had come for them to put their ideas to work. They decided to build a working model of a glider designed according to their own theories.

In May of 1900 they wrote to one of the most famous aviation scientists of the time, Octave Chanute. Chanute was perhaps the best informed aviation scientist in the United States. He had carried on glider experiments for many years. His book, *Progress in Flying Machines,* had been of great assistance to the brothers in their own research and study.

In their letter to Chanute, the brothers explained their theories and especially their concept of wing warping. Chanute's reply was encouraging. He suggested they find a likely spot on an ocean coast where they could test their ideas. He recommended the North Carolina coast. The Wrights wrote to the Weather Bureau Station at Kitty Hawk, North Carolina. The station's reply told them Kitty Hawk was exactly what they wanted—an average wind velocity of 15 miles per hour, and miles and miles of sand beaches and dunes.

During the summer of 1900 the two brothers spent most of their time constructing their first large glider. A childhood friend named Jammee Sines managed their bicycle business, allowing Orville and Wilbur the time they needed. During August they built the glider, sewing cloth for the wings, shaping the wooden frame, and making metal fasteners to hold the parts together.

Wilbur left for Kitty Hawk first, carrying with him all of the glider's parts except for long pieces of wood needed for the wings. These were acquired at Kitty Hawk. Orville arrived at the camp Wilbur had established and quickly the brothers assembled their machine.

They decided to test the glider first as a kite. The control surfaces were connected by wires to the operator's hands while he stood below.

Gleefully they discovered that their theory of wing warping was sound.

But something else was wrong.

Although the Wrights were certainly authentic geniuses, they were not expert mathematicians. They had made the mistake of blindly accepting the work of scientists better trained than they in physics and mathematics. They had designed their glider according to the scientific table and data developed by Lilienthal and other pioneers. The Wrights used this information in deciding how much surface area the wings of their glider should have and how much curve the wings should have from the leading (front) to trailing (rear) ends. Although their glider flew, its flight was erratic and surely unsafe.

They spent the fall of both 1900 and 1901 building and testing various models according to the data provided them by the earlier experimenters.

When they returned to Dayton in the winter of 1901, after their second season at Kitty Hawk, both brothers were discouraged. They knew now that if their efforts were to be successful, they would have to revise all of the mathematical tables they had used in their design.

"Maybe we're just chasing the wind," Orville told his brother one evening several days after they had returned to Dayton, following the discouraging tests at Kitty Hawk. "It will take months to develop new design data."

"I know," Wilbur answered. "And business at the bicycle shop is beginning to drop off a little, too. Jammee's doing a good job, but he can't handle all of it by himself."

"Do you think we ought to give it up?"

"I don't know," Wilbur said. "After all the work we've put into it I hate to just throw it all away. And besides . . ." His voice trailed off.

"Besides what?" Orville asked.

Wilbur grinned. "It sure would be great to be the first men to fly a powered airplane, wouldn't it?"

Orville grinned back. "Yes. It sure would."

With the help and encouragement of Octave Chanute the two brothers spent the winter of 1901-1902 developing new data. They constructed a small wind tunnel in which they tested nearly 200 wing surfaces of different design. It took several months of experiments before they finally collected all of the data they needed. Immediately they began to design a new glider and in the following August returned once again to that barren stretch of sand called Kitty Hawk.

Still as cautious as ever, they first tested the aircraft as a kite, controlling it with wires from the ground. It worked perfectly. They could raise or lower the glider at will. If a gust of wind pushed a wing down the operator easily restored it to level flight.

The long months of work had paid for itself. They had designed a perfectly controllable aircraft.

Delighted with the results of their own work, the two brothers spent October and November of 1902 making test flights. They made numerous glides. Their purpose was simple. They wanted to learn all they could about the art of piloting. They wanted to know how to handle the glider as easily as they handled bicycles; to be able to correct the flight of an airplane just as instinctively as a rider corrects the balance of his bicycle.

By the time they returned to Dayton they had flown nearly a thousand glider flights. The brothers came home elated with their accomplishments and anxious to begin the next big step.

"We've got the glider now," Orville told his sister, Kate. "It does everything we designed it to do."

"Now," added Wilbur, "all we have to do is add an engine and a propeller."

"Well," said Orville, "if that's all we need to do, let's start doing it."

They had hoped simply to purchase an engine and propeller. However, they could find no engine manufacturers willing to build to the specifications the Wrights listed. Nor could they find a propeller which even began to approach the kind Orville and Wilbur needed.

"Well," they concluded ruefully, "there's only one thing to do. We'll just build an engine and a propeller ourselves."

With their typical thoroughness and dedication, they did just that. At the end of September, 1903, they returned to Kitty Hawk. This time, they knew—*they knew*—that the great dream would become a reality and that they—the Wright brothers of Dayton, Ohio—would be the men who had done the impossible.

But the next two months at Kitty Hawk were filled with disappointments and setbacks. Arriving at their camp, they found that the hangar they had built previously was in bad shape. They set to work rebuilding it and then constructed another hangar nearby. In the meantime they also made numerous flights in their 1902 glider, getting as much experience as possible in controlling the craft in the air.

Then, during the first test of their new model, the new engine backfired and twisted one of the propeller shafts.

"The metal is too weak," Wilbur said after examining the twisted shaft. "We'll have to send both shafts back to Dayton and have them made from a stronger metal."

The brothers waited patiently for several weeks. When the new shafts arrived they were immediately installed in the two engines.

On the next test the brothers found that the engines vibrated so much that the nuts holding the engines in place worked loose very quickly. Characteristically, the brothers' natural inventiveness provided the answer. They applied bicycle tire cement to the engine bolt threads and then melted more cement on the nuts and bolts. The cement formed a perfectly tight bond and the nuts were tightened permanently.

But, now that the machine was at last ready for its first test, the weather turned against the two brothers. Winds screamed over their base at speeds of up to 75 miles an hour and threatened to blow everything—buildings, equipment, gliders—into the sea. Then suddenly the wind would disappear, and for long periods the base would be shrouded in a strange silence broken only by the sound of the waves.

During the second week in December, the two brothers waited impatiently for a good wind. For several days there had been none at all. Finally, on December 14, they decided to go ahead with a test. There was still no wind, but they decided to drag the plane to a nearby hillside. They hoped the craft could move down the side at sufficient speed to get off the ground.

Men from a life-saving station located on Kill Devil Hill not far from the brothers' camp helped drag the aircraft up the hill. The brothers had not yet put wheels on the machine. They had, instead, long runners which acted as skids to ease the plane on landings. For launching they constructed a 60-foot track. A small, wheeled cart ran on the track and the plane was mounted on the cart.

When the plane was placed on the track, Orville flipped a coin to see which brother would be first to try. Wilbur won.

He settled himself in the plane and warmed up the engines. Then he released a holding wire. The plane began to move forward. Orville ran alongside, holding the tip of the wing to keep the craft level until it gained enough speed to lift itself into the air.

But the plane moved faster than they had anticipated. About two-thirds of the way down the track it started to rise into the air and left Orville behind. Unexpectedly, the aircraft nosed up swiftly and then fell to the ground with a loud crunch.

On December 14, 1903, with Wilbur at the controls, the Wrights first attempted to put their aircraft into the sky. But shortly after this picture was taken, the airplane was damaged. The brothers set to work and were ready to try again three days later.

"Wilbur!" Orville yelled, running for the plane. He slowed as he saw his brother disentangle himself form the wreckage, rise and walk around the ship, shaking his head sadly as he surveyed the damage.

"Are you all right?" Orville panted as he reached his brother's side.

"Fine. Not a scratch. But look."

The left wing of the plane and one of the landing skids were broken.

Orville inspected the damage more closely. "It's not bad," he said. "Repair will be easy."

Wilbur nodded. "Well, let's get at it then."

They spent the next two days repairing the ship and waiting for the right kind of wind. On the night of December 16 they lay in their cots listening to a boisterous December wind whip around the building outside.

"Wilbur." Orville said in the darkness. "Are you awake?"

"Yes."

"I think we ought to try it tomorrow no matter what the weather is like. What do you say?"

There was only a moment's pause. "I say yes. Tomorrow's the day."

There was a few minutes of silence as both lay listening to the roar of the raw wind.

"Christmas is only a week away," Orville said softly. Wilbur could sense that his brother's thoughts were hundreds of miles away, back in Dayton.

"Yes," Orville declared. "Tomorrow *will* be the day."

The next morning they arose and looked outside at the bleak sand dunes around their camp. The wind still whistled past the hangar. Puddles of rainwater in the sand were crusted with a thin layer of ice.

The brothers ate their breakfasts and waited, hoping the wind would die down. But it continued through the morning and showed no signs of dying.

It was 10:00 A.M. "Well," said Orville. "What do you think?"

"Let's go ahead," Wilbur said.

Men from the life-saving station were called and they set about preparing the plane. This time they set up the track on level ground, facing it into the wind. The brothers felt that with such a wind, blowing gusts up to 27 miles per hour, they could certainly make a flight from a horizontal track.

Orville took his position and started the engine.

He turned his head, grinned at Wilbur and released the holding wire.

The plane moved slowly into the wind. Wilbur easily stayed with it. As on the previous flight, the plane rose into the air about forty feet from its starting point. As it did, one of the men from the life-saving station snapped the shutter of a camera that the Wrights had positioned before the flight. This historic picture (reproduced on the facing page) shows the plane a few feet off the ground. It is a photographic record of the first powered airplane flight in the history of the world.

For twelve long, delicious seconds, Wilbur stood at the end of the track watching as Orville fought to control the flight in the gusty wind. In the air, Orville found the controls of the plane so delicate that when he altered the angle of the controls only a little the plane rose or fell with alarming speed. Then he depressed one of the controls too much and the plane "landed" abruptly.

The flight had lasted 12 seconds and covered a distance of 120 feet.

One of the most dramatic moments in the history of aviation was captured by the camera as Orville Wright began the first successful flight in a man-controlled, engine-powered aircraft at Kitty Hawk, N.C. At right is Wilbur Wright.

They had done it! The dream of centuries had come true. An airplane—with a man at its controls—had actually lifted itself from the ground and flown.

The brothers quickly hauled the plane back to the launching ramp. This time Wilbur took a turn. His flight nearly equaled Orville's in time and distance.

Although delighted with their success, the short distances disappointed the brothers. They knew the problem was not with the aircraft. It was because of their inexperience in controlling the aircraft. On Orville's next flight, he stayed in the air 15 seconds and traveled 200 feet. At noon Wilbur made a fourth flight and this time, *this time,* the craft stayed in the air for nearly a full minute and traveled 852 feet.

After the fourth flight, the brothers and the men from the life-saving station gathered around the aircraft elatedly discussing the last trip. Suddenly a giant gust of wind picked the plane up and turned it over and over. It was badly damaged and could not be flown again immediately.

But even this setback did not dampen the brothers' high spirits. They had achieved what they had set out to do. They had solved the problem of flying and controlling a powered aircraft.

The Wrights returned to Dayton.

Sadly enough, it took several more years before the United States accepted the truth of the Wright brothers' accomplishment. The average man in those days did not believe that airplanes could fly. "And even if they could," many men said, "they're nothing but toys."

But in 1907, after years of painstaking research and constant refinement of their original design, the brothers made a barnstorming tour of Europe. They flew their aircraft before thousands of delighted Europeans. The success of this

In 1908 the Wright brothers demonstrated their aircraft for the U. S. Army at Fort Myer, Virginia. This was a record-setting flight—the first flight in history over one hour.

tour reached the newspapers in the United States and finally the brothers achieved their long-deserved fame, honor and reward.

On May 30, 1912, Wilbur Wright died of typhoid fever. Neither brother had married and now Orville was left alone. But devoted nephews and nieces brightened his life, and he became the elder statesman of aviation until his death on January 30, 1948.

Today, great jet airplanes skimming across the blue sky, leaving behind wispy trails of vapor to mark their paths, are a common sight. Man has achieved what just seventy years ago were seemingly impossible dreams. It began on that bleak stretch of barren sand off the North Carolina coast at a place called Kitty Hawk.

Part III

Wings

I T was done.

Man had won. A new frontier lay before him: the unexplored sky. And it was his to explore.

Kitty Hawk had been a great battle. Wilbur and Orville Wright were indeed the victors. But before man could truly call himself master of the sky, there were still many battles ahead.

When word of the Wrights' achievement at Kitty Hawk reached Europe, most people refused to believe it. They still thought that flight was impossible. For several years after that cold December day at Kitty Hawk, the two brothers and their work remained nearly unknown.

During the first decade of the twentieth century, hundreds of aviation pioneers continued their research and experiments. Among them was the dapper Albert Santos-Dumont. In 1906 his name once again echoed across Europe. A few years before, he had turned his attention to the challenge of heavier-than-air flight. With his everlasting conviction that "what is logical is possible," he began a series of experiments, first with gliders, then with powered biplanes.

In August, 1906, Santos-Dumont became the first man to
fly a powered airplane in Europe. Again the famous aviator
was hailed as a hero. His flight was believed to be the first in
the world. The following year, 1907, the Wright brothers
brought their latest model aircraft to France. They amazed
Europe with their astounding machine and convinced the
world that they were, in truth, the first of their kind.

Now that the airplane had become reality, what else
needed to be done? There was only one answer. The machines of the Wrights and other pioneers could fly only short
distances and at low altitudes. Now, new designs must be
developed so that longer distances and higher altitudes could
be achieved.

Between 1906 and 1910 world interest in the new science
grew steadily. Almost every month new altitude and distance
records were established.

The pioneers piled experiment upon experiment. And
with each new discovery, their fragile little aircraft, most
made of light wooden frames and fabric surfaces, flew higher
and further.

As always, in Lilienthal's words, "the wind and air must
have their say in the matter." The pioneers could study, they
could plan, they could build. But to prove their ideas, they
had to fly.

It was as though the sky were saying: "I am still here. You
have invaded my bounds, but I am still not conquered. For
complete victory you must pay a terrible price—the constant
risk of death. Am I worth such a price?"

"Yes!" replied the skymasters. "YES!"

And among them, answering with the loudest cry of all,
was a man destined to make one of the most startling flights
in aviation history: Louis Bleriot of France.

"Where Is Dover?"

IT WAS TO BE A QUIET EVENING at home. Or at least Madame Bleriot had expected it to be. Now, she didn't know.

She and her husband, Louis, sat in the drawing room of their gracious home at the outskirts of Orleans in north central France. It was a beautiful town with wide boulevards, handsome squares and ancient buildings.

Louis suddenly rose from his chair. He stalked to the fireplace and stood there, drumming his fingers impatiently on the marble mantle.

Madame Bleriot set aside the book she had been reading. "Louis, what *is* the matter with you? Are you angry? Has something gone wrong at the factory?"

He turned to face her, surprise on his face. Then he grinned as though embarrassed. "I am sorry. I do not mean to cause you worry. No, there is nothing wrong at the factory. Perhaps that is what is wrong. Perhaps it all goes too well."

"Well, what is it then?" she asked. "In the past few weeks you have grown more restless with each new day. What is troubling you?"

Louis locked his hands behind his back. He began to pace the floor in front of the fireplace.

He did not answer her immediately. But she knew he would. Yes, she knew this man, Louis Bleriot, and loved him deeply. He was a stocky, handsome man with reddish hair and a thick red mustache that he kept neatly trimmed. He was a brilliant man. He possessed a keen analytical mind that could scrape away unnecessary details of a problem to get at its basic cause.

The world already knew Louis Bleriot as a success. In this year of 1900 he was only twenty-eight years old. Yet he already had become moderately wealthy. He was a student of engineering and a graduate of the Technical School of France, one of that country's most famous universities.

That new invention called the automobile was gaining increased popularity across France. Young Bleriot had recognized that the new industry was going to continue to boom. He had turned his engineering ability and inventive talents to it. He invented a unique kind of automobile headlight. Soon afterward he established a factory at Orleans to produce his invention. Later he expanded the business with additional automobile accessories.

Yes, beyond a doubt Louis Bleriot had achieved success as well as fortune. But the Louis Bleriot who paced back and forth in front of the marble fireplace did not look like a picture of success. Indeed, he did not look at all like the man Madame Bleriot knew as her husband. My Louis is a great, smiling man who loves to laugh as much as he loves to take risks, she thought. He is a man who would rather sit on a fast horse than behind a desk.

She smiled to herself. How many times, as he had pushed their automobile to its top speed, had she asked him to slow down. And always there came his broad smile and his instant apology. "I am sorry, *ma chérie*. I forget at times that you do not like the high speeds. I shall not do it again."

But, of course, he would soon come to a place in the road where he could push the car to its top speed. She would remind him gently and he would apologize and promise not to speed again . . . until the next time.

Yes, she told herself, that is my husband. He is a man who must have new challenges every day.

Louis stopped pacing. He returned to the chair across from her. "My wife, I have reached a decision. I am going to sell the factory."

Her eyes widened. "Sell the . . .?"

He nodded vigorously. "Yes, I have had several offers for it, some of them for a very high price."

"But why? What is the matter?" Madame Bleriot cast a look around the comfortably furnished room. "We have been so happy here."

His face became more intent. "Listen to me carefully. For the past few years I have been following this new science called aviation very carefully. Great things are being accomplished. Before very long there will be a big breakthrough.

"Think of it! Man will be able to fly. He will be able to take to the sky like an albatross and spread his wings and travel great distances." Bleriot's eyes shone with excitement. "I want to be part of that, my wife. I want to share in this new world of the sky! It is almost open to us. There are many great men working on the problem. I want to join them in their work. I *must* join them."

Madame Bleriot studied her husband. She heard the excitement in his voice, saw it in his eyes and in the electric tension of his body. Yes, she repeated to herself, my husband is a man who must have challenges. That is what is wrong with the factory. It is done, over with. He has mastered his inventions, sold them, and made a great deal of money. The challenge is gone now. He needs a new one.

"Louis, if this new business called aviation is what you want, then that is what you should have. If it is what you believe you must do, that is what I want too," she said.

Louis leaped from his chair, whooping with joy. He pulled his wife to her feet and danced her around the room, laughing happily. *"Ma chérie,"* he boomed, "we will make the birds weep with envy!"

He wasted no time in selling his factory, and within a few short months he moved his wife and household to Paris. Then he began the long months of study that he knew were so important to his success in the business of flying.

Bleriot's first experiments were with gliders. These were equipped with various mechanical devices that made the wings of the aircraft flap up and down, in imitation of bird flight. He soon realized this was a mistake and turned his attention to the fixed-wing glider. Like Lilienthal and the Wright brothers he realized that control of the aircraft in flight was the first thing to master.

The years between 1900 and 1906 were extremely difficult for Louis. His many experiments with new concepts of airplane control slowly drained away his moderate fortune. His wife remained at his side, helping to manage his money, encouraging him when he became despondent, and nursing his injuries.

And there were many injuries. The stocky Frenchman with the red mustache became famous for his accidents. His friends, knowing his recklessness, predicted he would be killed. Through it all he displayed such fearlessness that he earned the admiration of all who knew of him and his work.

He was once asked how he managed to survive his numerous crashes, many of which had completely destroyed his aircraft. "In case of an accident," he replied casually, "I throw myself on one of the wings. That, of course, breaks the wing, but it saves me."

During the first few years after the turn of the century glider flight had become extremely popular. A great many

French Embassy Press & Information Division

Louis Bleriot

Aero clubs were formed in Europe as well as in the United States. Their purpose was to promote the science of aviation. Here aviators could exchange information about flying. Many newspapers in France, Europe and the United States devoted attention to the increasingly popular sport. They often offered large sums of prize money to the first aviators to achieve a new distance or altitude record.

In 1905 Louis entered a partnership with the Voisin brothers, early French aviation pioneers. The Voisins had already established themselves as manufacturers of gliders. The partners turned their attention to the problems of powered flight and designed a powered bi-plane. They entered the aircraft in competition for a $10,000 prize for the first airplane flight of a full kilometer in a circle. However, on the first attempt, with Louis at the controls, the craft smashed into an obstacle on the ground and was destroyed by the impact.

Bleriot coolly extracted himself from the wreckage. A crowd had rushed to the scene, among them his partners, the Voisin brothers. "Shall we return to the factory and build another?" Louis asked them calmly.

Gabriel Voisin put his arm across Bleriot's shoulder and grinned. "Of course, Louis. That is the only thing left to do, is it not?"

"Of course," replied Louis. They left the field, arm in arm, immediately lost in a discussion of how the next model should be designed. Madame Bleriot followed, her eyes traveling from the wreckage behind her, to her husband, and then upwards as she murmured her thousandth prayer of thanks.

As the months passed, however, Louis became more and more convinced that the double-winged airplane, so popular at the time, lacked the agility he believed an aircraft should have in the air. He felt the single-wing design—the monoplane—had many more advantages. The Voisin brothers, however, did not share his belief. Louis decided to leave the partnership and devote his full energies to the single-wing concept.

By July, 1907, only seven months after the failure to win the $10,000, Louis had constructed his first monoplane. On its first flight it flew 86 yards, and for once, Louis landed safely. Immediately he began to re-design the plane, correcting the faults he had discovered during the flight.

By December he was ready. Once again Madame Bleriot stood at the side of a little airfield outside Paris. She watched as he moved the plane into the wind. The engine roared as he sped forward. Gracefully the little aircraft climbed into the air.

Madame Bleriot heaved a sigh of relief. Perhaps it was going to be a success. Now, at last, Louis could——

A sharp, brittle cracking sound broke her thought. What was that? She looked upward and froze in horror. Both wings of the aircraft had snapped off. The body of the plane hurtled to the ground and struck with a deafening crash.

"Louis! Louis!" She ran toward the wreckage. She had watched Louis crash many times. But none were as bad as this. Several men who had seen the crash ran to help her.

Louis was sitting on the ground a few yards from the twisted wreckage. He was carefully moving his arms and legs. The men helped him to his feet. He surveyed his smashed aircraft and then limped to his wife. "A few bad bruises, that is all I suffer. But my poor aircraft. It is completely gone. To build another I will have to start from the beginning."

Madame Bleriot stared at him, her concern mingled with exasperation. "Louis," she began, and then stopped.

"Yes, *ma chérie?*" he said, looking at her quizzically.

"Nothing," she answered. "Come. Let us go home now. After you are rested we can start on the next one."

"I think I know what went wrong," he said as they walked off the field toward their car. "I did not include the proper support for the wings. The forward movement through the air was too much for them. Now, if I add reinforcement to the joint between the wings and the body of the plane . . ."

"Yes, dear," she replied, helping him into the car.

Ten months later the new model was ready. Once again his wife stood at the edge of the field as he taxied into position and roared into the wind.

Louis had designated this model the *Bleriot XI*. It closely resembled airplanes of today: single wings, a long graceful fuselage, and a tail assembly consisting of a vertical rudder and horizontal stabilizers. Almost all of the successful aircraft of that era were biplanes with very little fuselage. Often the stabilizers were located in front of the wings.

Another notable Bleriot advancement was the use of a "tractor" type propeller. Located in the nose of the plane, it pulled the aircraft through the air. It was one of the first of its kind. Most other planes used a "pusher" type propeller located behind the wings.

These were Louis Bleriot's most significant contributions to the science of aviation: lightweight, monoplane design and the "tractor" type propeller. It was many years before the monoplane was accepted as superior to the traditional double-winged design.

But none of these thoughts were in the mind of Madame Bleriot as she watched the *Bleriot XI* roar into the air.

Higher and higher it climbed, until she could hardly see the figure of her husband at the controls.

Then it began a long, gliding circle, gently lowering itself to the earth. On the ground, it traveled for a few yards and then stopped.

Louis leaped from the cockpit, ran from the plane and stopped to turn and stare at it. Madame Bleriot reached his side. He put his arm around her shoulder. "Eight and a half minutes," he said, awe in his voice. "It flew for eight and a half minutes."

During the next few months, Louis continued to modify the *Bleriot XI*. During late 1908 and early 1909 he made longer and longer flights. There were still accidents, still setbacks. But with his usual determination and careless disregard for danger he was soon back in the air.

The years 1908 and 1909 seemed to be the years that the science of aviation was waiting for. By then the Wright brothers had finally gained their long-deserved recognition. The world of flying blossomed. Men all over Europe and the United States began to build and fly powered airplanes. Each week, new records in distance and altitudes were set. Pilots flew exhibition flights that drew gasps of amazement from crowds in many nations of Europe. Competitive flying grew in popularity.

It was in France, however, that most of the activity continued to be centered. The names of the men who flew the fragile-looking aircraft were known in every household. Among them the name of Louis Bleriot shared equal fame.

Several of these famous pilots established flying schools, Louis included. He also established a factory and began producing and selling his airplanes.

And he continued to fly. In November, 1908, he succeeded

in a flight that lasted for 37 minutes. His next air journey was a flight across country covering 25 miles in 43 minutes. His fame continued to spread.

During this period another French aviator also achieved world fame. His name was Hubert Latham, a slender young man of tremendous courage and daring.

In late 1909 a London newspaper, the *Daily Mail*, offered a $5,000 prize for the first flight across the English Channel, between England and France. The prospect of such a flight chilled the hearts of the less adventurous aviators. It was one thing to risk life and limb over the ground; at least there you had a good chance to survive. But to crash in the icy waters of the English Channel? And the winds, what about the winds? Gentle breezes caressing the slopes and trees on the countryside below were of valuable help to the pilot. But the rough, boisterous winds that swept the Channel were impossible. No aircraft could fly in them.

Three men responded to the *Daily Mail*'s prize offer. One of them, Count de Lambert of France, later was forced to drop out. The second was Hubert Latham. The third, Louis Bleriot.

Latham and Bleriot were well acquainted. The fraternity of the early aviators was small. They all knew and respected each other because they shared two common bonds—the determination that man should master the sky and the willingness to die to make the great dream reality.

Latham had been born in England. But he lived most of his life in France and considered himself a Frenchman. A young man with great courage, he was one of the most popular aviators of the age.

When Bleriot learned that Latham, too, intended to compete for the Channel flight, he shook his head regretfully. "If there is any man who can make the trip, it is Latham," Louis told his wife. "The man is absolutely fearless."

Louis spent the next few days preparing the *Bleriot XI*. Then, on a cross-country flight to test a modification to the plane's engine, disaster struck. The engine failed. The plane plummeted to the ground, crashed and burst into flames. Louis escaped, but his leg was burned badly.

He returned to Paris on crutches and immediately began to prepare another *Bleriot XI* for the Channel flight.

His wife stared in amazement when he declared that he still intended to make the flight. "But Louis," she protested, "you cannot. Your leg. I can tell by your face that you are in pain. Please, don't be foolish."

"I must," he said grimly.

"But why? Can it be that important?"

Louis nodded. "Yes, it is. To fly across the English Channel is to prove to the world that the airplane is no mere toy. There are still many people who think that aviation is just another sport. The Channel flight will open their eyes. It will show that the airplane has made the world smaller. They will realize that we no longer have to spend hours and hours traveling from one place to another.

"And I, Louis Bleriot, wish to be the one to do this."

As always, Madame Bleriot conceded. Louis hastened to his aircraft factory to urge his mechanics to work faster in readying the plane.

Then, on July 23, 1909, before the craft was completely ready, Louis received startling news. Latham was in the air! He had left Calais, a French coastal town, that morning, headed across the Channel toward Dover, England.

Louis groaned. For hours he waited impatiently for the results of Latham's flight. His mechanics asked if they should continue working on the *Bleriot XI*.

"Of course!" Louis answered. "Latham may be the first, but Louis Bleriot will be the second. Keep working!"

Hours passed. Then a man ran into Louis's office. "Latham failed," he announced. "He crashed into the Channel. He is safe. The patrol boats rescued him and are returning him to Calais. They say he intends to get another plane and try again."

"What a fabulous man!" cried Louis. "Nothing will stop him."

But Louis did not allow his admiration for his competitor to interfere with his own plans. He urged his mechanics on to greater effort. "Hurry," he said. "Hurry. Latham will try again as soon as he can. I know he will."

The *Bleriot XI* was ready the next day. In the meantime Latham returned and obtained another airplane and now waited in Calais for favorable weather. Louis flew his aircraft to Calais and made final preparations.

But then great storm clouds settled over the French coast. Riotous winds swept across the Channel, turning the icy water into foam and waves. Flight was impossible, even for the little *Bleriot XI*. Louis waited impatiently.

On Sunday morning, July 25, he awakened early. The pain from his burned leg would not let him sleep. It was about 2:30 A.M. He dressed quickly and used his crutches to hobble outside into the French night. The wind had stopped, but the stars and moon were still obscured by a layer of clouds and misty fog.

Madame Bleriot was not with him. She was on one of the naval ships that the French government had placed at the disposal of Bleriot and Latham. The ships were to rescue the pilots if they crashed, as Latham already had done. Madame Bleriot was now aboard the French destroyer, *Escopette,* awaiting news of Louis's flight.

Louis drove to the airfield. He found everything in order and took off on a trial flight around Calais. Then he returned to the airfield and landed.

Latham's mechanics had seen Bleriot return. They made a mistake that Latham was to regret for the rest of his life. The mechanics did not realize that Bleriot's short flight was simply a test. They assumed that he was not going to fly again that day. Believing this, they did not awaken Latham, who was still asleep a short while later when Louis returned and took his place in the cockpit of the *Bleriot XI.*

As he prepared to start his engine, Louis called to one of his mechanics beside the plane, "Where is Dover?"

The mechanic pointed across the Channel and grinned broadly. Louis grinned back.

Later, Louis wrote an article for the London *Daily Mail* and described what had happened next:

> I waited for the sun to come out, the conditions of the *Daily Mail* prize requiring that I fly between sunrise and sunset. At 4:30 daylight had come, but it was impossible to see the coast. A light breeze from the southwest was blowing the air clear, however, and everything was prepared.
>
> I was dressed in a khaki jacket lined with wool for warmth over my tweed clothes and beneath my engineer's suit of blue cotton overalls. A close-fitting cap was fastened over my head and ears. I had neither eaten nor drunk anything since I rose. My thoughts were only upon the flight and my determination to accomplish it that morning.
>
> At 4:35 "All's ready." My friend Le Blanche gives the

Standing in the cockpit of his staunch little Bleriot XI, Louis Bleriot makes a final check of his aircraft just before taking off from Calais, France, on an aerial journey that startled the world.

signal, and in an instant I am in the air, my engine making 1,200 revolutions, almost its highest speed, in order that I may get quickly over the telegraph wires along the edge of the cliff.

As soon as I am over the cliff I reduce speed. There was now no need to force the engine. I began my flight, steady and sure, toward the coast of England. I had no apprehensions, no sensation—*pas du tout*—not at all.

The *Escopette* has seen me. She is driving ahead at full speed. She makes perhaps 42 kilometers [26 miles an hour]. What matters it? I am making at least 68 kilometers [over 42 miles an hour]. Rapidly I overtake her traveling at a height of 80 meters [260 feet]. Below me is the surface of the sea, disturbed by the wind, which is now freshening. The motion of the waves beneath me is not pleasant. I drive on.

Ten minutes are gone. I have passed the destroyer, and I turn my head to see whether I am proceeding in the right direction. I am amazed. There is nothing to be seen— neither the torpedo boat destroyer nor France nor England.

I am alone; I can see nothing at all.

For ten minutes I am lost; it is a strange position to be in—alone, guided without a compass in the air over the middle of the Channel. I touch nothing, my hands and feet rest lightly on the levers. I let the aeroplane take its own course. I care not whither it goes.

For ten minutes I continue, neither rising nor falling nor turning, and—then, twenty minutes after I have left the French coast, I see green cliffs and Dover Castle, and away to the west the spot where I had intended to land.

What can I do? It is evident the wind has taken me out of my course. I am almost at St. Margaret's Bay, going in the direction of Goodwin Sands.

Now is the time to attend to the steering. I press a lever

with my foot and turn easily toward the west, reversing the direction in which I am traveling.

Now I am in difficulties, for the wind here by the cliffs is much stronger and my speed is reduced as I fight against it, yet my beautiful aeroplane responds still steadily.

I fly westward, chopping across the harbor, and reach Shakespeare Cliff. I see an opening in the cliff. Although I am confident I can continue for an hour and a half, that I might, indeed, return to Calais, I cannot resist the opportunity to make a landing upon this green spot.

Once more I turn my aeroplane, and, describing a half circle, I enter the opening and find myself again over dry land. Avoiding the red buildings on my right, I attempt a landing, but the wind catches me and whirls me around two or three times. At once I stop my motor, and instantly my machine falls straight upon the ground from a height of twenty meters [75 feet]. In two or three seconds I am safe upon the shore.

Soldiers in khaki run up, and policemen. Two of my compatriots are on the spot. They kiss my cheeks. The conclusion of my flight overwhelms me.

Thus ended my flight across the Channel—a flight which could easily be done again. Shall I do it? I think not. I have promised my wife that after this race for which I have already entered I will fly no more.

Friends had been waiting at the field where Bleriot landed. Choked with emotion they took the still-limping aviator to a Dover hotel. A great crowd gathered outside shouting the Frenchman's name. Then the *Escopette* arrived. Madame Bleriot was delivered to the hotel. Weeping with joy she embraced her husband.

The mayor of Dover and other city officials arrived at the hotel and welcomed Louis in the name of their city and their

The monoplane design of Bleriot's aircraft was very rare for 1909; yet all modern aircraft have single wings.

nation. When the news of his flight reached France that nation exploded with delirious joy. The French government gave Louis the Legion of Honor, and the newspapers acclaimed him a great hero. Hundreds of congratulatory telegrams poured in from all over the world.

Through it all Louis maintained his usual calm. The evening of the flight, he and Madame Bleriot returned to Calais by boat and were escorted to a hotel where a large party was held in their honor. After many long speeches by government officials and other dignitaries, Louis finally stood up. "All I can say is that I am radiantly happy at my success. I am also happy that I have received the decoration of the Legion of Honor."

Then he sat down and held Madame Bleriot's hand as the crowd rose to its feet and cheered him.

Bleriot's famous flight across the Channel was certainly not the last of this brave aviator's exploits. For the rest of his life, until his death in 1936, he devoted his energies and talents to aviation, designing more and more modern aircraft. Through the following years thousands of Bleriot aircraft left his factories and took to the skies.

Shortly after Bleriot's feat, the Wright brothers heard the news. They described his journey as "remarkable."

Perhaps that is the best way to describe Louis Bleriot and his courageous flight: a remarkable journey by a remarkable man.

The Lone Eagle

I T WAS a typical weekday morning in a small Nebraska farm town. Housewives were shopping. Small children played tag in the dusty streets. Several farmers stood in front of the local feed and grain store discussing crops. Three old men sat in comfortable chairs on the veranda of the town's only hotel, relaxing beneath the warm summer sun.

Suddenly a strange noise intruded upon the tranquil scene. It sounded like the drone of an angry hornet, and it came from the sky.

The people looked up. There, a few hundred feet above the town, a sleek two-winged airplane sped past.

"My gosh!" exclaimed one man. "Lookit that! There's a guy standing on the wing of that airplane."

Sure enough, a man was stepping carefully over the wires and struts that braced the aircraft's two wings. The plane banked and returned. As it passed overhead the man waved to the people below.

More people emerged from the stores, and the crowd grew

rapidly. Every face was turned upward, watching the aircraft and its daring passenger perform.

Then the plane turned and headed for the edge of the town.

"C'mon!" yelled a young boy. "It's going to land in the field." He and several of his friends dashed down the street.

"Who are they? What are they doing here?" a woman asked as the crowd began to disperse toward the field.

"Barnstormers," replied a man walking beside her. "Stunt pilots. They travel all over the country from town to town doing tricks and selling airplane rides."

Within a few minutes the crowd reached the field. There stood the airplane. Its propeller whirled invisibly at its nose. The plane had two seats, one just behind the wings and another further back along the fuselage. A pilot sat in the rear seat.

A man stood beside the wing. He and the other pilot were dressed similarly. Both wore tight-fitting knee-high cavalry boots, baggy riding pants, jackets, and leather flying helmets.

The man beside the plane had been the wingwalker. He stepped forward as the crowd approached. He was tall and boyish looking, with a friendly smile. "All right, folks, who would like to take a ride? The price is only five dollars and the thrill is one you'll never forget. It's absolutely safe and there's nothing to be afraid of. Now who wants to be first?"

No one answered at first. They just looked at the airplane and the pilot curiously. Again he assured them of the safety of flight.

"Well," said one man in the front of the crowd, "I guess if you can walk on that darned thing, I can sit in it."

He stepped forward and paid his five dollars. With a big grin the young pilot gave him a few instructions about safety.

The customer walked to the craft and climbed in the front seat. In a few minutes the machine was in the air, its passenger waving to the crowd below.

"Who's next?" the pilot asked loudly. "Form a line over here, folks. Remember, it's just five dollars for the thrill of a lifetime."

Within a short while a line had formed. The airplane returned with its first passenger. He stepped to the ground and was immediately surrounded by friends who wanted to know what it felt like to fly. The next passenger took his seat in the front cockpit. Again the plane took to the air.

The rest of the day passed quickly. By evening a large number of people had taken their first airplane ride. Only a few small boys were still in the field at dusk, watching with envy as the plane took off. It quickly disappeared into the horizon, headed for another town.

The men and women who had flown with the barnstormers that day probably recalled the event for the rest of their lives. It was an experience they could never forget. Perhaps some of them learned the identity of the boyish looking aviator who had walked on the wing. And if, a few years later, they remembered his name, the memory of meeting him was to be even more cherished.

He was Charles Lindbergh. In 1927 he made a flight that brought the world to its feet shouting and cheering his name. This single aerial journey established the world of aviation as we know it today. It was perhaps the most important flight in history.

By 1922, when the barnstorming plane visited the little Nebraska farm community, aviation seemed to have come full circle. Following Bleriot's Channel flight in 1910, aviation had spurted forward. New altitudes and longer distances were gained. Newer, better powered, better designed air-planes were developed.

World War I stimulated even faster development. The great fighter pilots of the war and their speedy, agile air-planes became international heroes.

But when the war ended, the importance of the airplane dwindled, especially in the United States. A few of the more farsighted aviators continued working and designing better aircraft. But the general public believed that with the end of the war the airplane had lost its usefulness. Only those few aviators knew that the potential of aviation was not as yet fully realized. Once again a great accomplishment was needed to reawaken world interest.

Onto this scene stepped the young man named Charles Lindbergh.

He was twenty years old when he walked into the office of the president of the Nebraska Aircraft Corporation at Lincoln, Nebraska, and solemnly announced that he would like to enroll in the company's flying school.

The owner of the company studied the young man before him. He saw a tall, gawky country boy with blond hair and light blue eyes inherited from his Swedish ancestors.

He was skeptical. "It will cost five hundred dollars, cash," he said.

Immediately and quietly Lindbergh paid the fee, and a new way of life opened to him, a life quite different from the one he had lived until that day in 1922.

Lindbergh was born in 1902 in Detroit, Michigan, and was taken to his family's farm at Little Falls, Minnesota. His grandparents had settled in that state in 1859. The Lindbergh name was well known in the area. His father, a lawyer, was a member of the United States Congress. Charles spent most of his boyhood traveling between Washington and Minnesota. By the time he reached adulthood he was accustomed to travel.

In 1920 he entered the University of Wisconsin, intending to study mechanical engineering. But in his second year he decided to give that up in favor of aviation, and he enrolled in a flying school in Lincoln, Nebraska.

The willingness to make a decision and then follow it immediately with action was perhaps the most outstanding part of Charles Lindbergh's personality. It is true that he was a soft-spoken, almost bashful man. But once he made up his mind to do something, he did it, even if danger were involved. Consequently, neither his parents nor his friends were able to talk him out of his decision to enter aviation.

Until he arrived at the flying school in Lincoln, Lindbergh had never so much as touched an airplane. Shortly after he had enrolled and paid the tuition, he stood on the airfield looking at the plane in which he was to take his first ride. Years later, in his famous book, *The Spirit of St. Louis*, he recorded the thoughts that passed through his mind as mechanics prepared the craft for the flight:

> Behind every movement, word, and detail, one felt the strength of life, the presence of death. There was pride in man's conquest of the air. There was the realization that he took life in hand to fly, that in each bolt and wire and wooden strut death lay imprisoned like the bottled genie ... An error meant a ship might crash; a man might die. I stood aside and watched the engine tested, watched the plane taxi out, take off, and then spiral up through the sky. I'd be on the next flight, if this test showed nothing wrong. I'd be part of those wings, now no longer than a bird's, black against the clouds toward which they climbed.

The plane returned. Lindbergh and another young student took their places in the front cockpit. The engine was started and the plane taxied out onto the runway. There was a brief hesitation as the pilot in the rear seat checked his gauges for a final time. Then, with a powerful roar of its engine, the plane lurched forward.

Lindbergh recalled his first flight in his book:

> Trees become bushes; barns, toys; cows turn into rabbits as we climb. . . . I live only in the moment in this strange, unmortal space, crowded with beauty, pierced with danger. The horizon retreats, and veils itself in haze. The great, squared fields of Nebraska become patchwork on a planet's disk. All the country around Lincoln lies like a relief map below...

And so the young man from Minnesota was introduced to the world above. But it was more than a mere meeting. It was the start of a great romance between the man and the sky.

The next month passed quickly. Lindbergh received several hours of flight training and spent much of his time in the factory helping build and repair the airplanes of the company sponsoring the flying school. This experience taught him a great deal about the care and maintenance of airplanes. This was something he had to know, because he had already decided to take up the life of a barnstormer.

But before he completed his flying instructions, the aircraft company decided to sell the training plane. Lindbergh heard that the man who bought it intended to take it on a barnstorming tour. Lindbergh asked to be taken along. The man agreed, and for the next month Lindbergh flew with him. It was during this trip that Lindbergh walked his first wing. It was a trick that always drew attention and got customers for plane rides when the plane passed over a town.

After the trip Lindbergh returned to Lincoln and obtained a job at the aircraft factory. One day a parachute maker arrived in town. Lindbergh stood at the edge of the field and watched in fascination as the man leaped from a plane 2,000 feet over the ground.

With typical Lindbergh single-mindedness, he decided that he, too, wanted to make a parachute jump. The anticipation of the experience thrilled him. He *had* to do it.

Why? What purpose could there be in throwing yourself from a plane and trusting your life to a piece of muslin cloth and some long cords?

The reason, Lindbergh wrote in his book, was the quality that led him into aviation in the first place: It was

> . . . a love of the air and sky and flying, the lure of adventure, the appreciation of beauty . . . where life meets death on equal plane; where man is more than man, and existence both supreme and valueless at the same instant.

He sought out the parachute maker and made his first jump the next day. It was everything he had expected it to be, and more. From that moment on he considered himself an aviator.

During the next two years he pitched himself headlong into the life of the barnstormer. Following his first parachute jump he joined forces with another flier and traveled the Midwest performing wingwalking stunts and parachute jumps. Then he bought his first aircraft, a military surplus plane called the *Jenny*. For the next year he barnstormed, flying from town to town selling rides.

Although Lindbergh was a daring pilot, the risks he took

were seldom foolish. He believed that careful observance of the rules and a cool head in time of danger could make the difference between life and death. He was willing to try something new only when he was flying by himself. He never endangered the lives of his passengers with foolish stunts and was always careful to keep his plane in the best possible condition.

In spite of the care he took with his aircraft there were still many accidents, some of them nearly comic, others almost fatal. Occasionally even the near-fatal crashes took a comic turn. In later years Lindbergh remembered them with fond amusement.

On one occasion he landed in the town square of a small community. Airports in the 1920's were nearly non-existent. The barnstormers often landed in the most convenient spot. It had to be one which allowed them ample room to build up enough speed to take off again.

When Lindbergh was ready to leave the town he realized that to take off he would have to run the plane between two telephone poles at the end of the square. He measured the distance between the poles. It was 48 feet. The wingspan of his plane was 46 feet.

Well, if I'm careful, he told himself, I can make it with two feet to spare. He increased the speed of his engine and the plane shot forward toward the poles.

Unfortunately, Lindbergh had not noticed a depression in the ground. The plane's wheels struck it and swerved off the intended path. The craft shot forward. Its wing struck one of the posts. The plane spun wildly across the ground and then dove into a hardware store.

The owner of the store had been attending to his business when suddenly he heard and felt a great crash. He looked up in amazement to discover part of an airplane sticking through the front wall of the store. And there, almost buried beneath a jumble of pots and pans, was the pilot, slowly climbing out of the cockpit.

"Good lord, man!" said the storekeeper, rushing up to the plane. "Are you hurt?"

Lindbergh assured the man that he was not injured. In the meantime the townspeople came running. They stood around and gaped at the airplane sticking out of the store.

The plane was removed and repaired. Lindbergh offered to pay the storekeeper for the damage.

"No such thing," said the storekeeper. "Your crashing in was great advertising. People will come from all over to see where it happened. So never you mind about paying. The new customers I'll be getting will more than pay for the damage."

A few hours later Lindbergh was in the air again, heading for his next destination.

In 1924 Lindbergh sold his *Jenny* and enrolled in the United States Army Air Service. A year later he was graduated as a lieutenant in the Army reserve and as a full-fledged military pilot. By this time he had acquired nearly 2,000 hours of flying time. In those days, the life span of pilots was measured in terms of hours in the air. The average pilot flew 900 hours before he was either killed or maimed in a crash.

Lindbergh's great skill as a pilot was demonstrated several months after graduation from the Air Training Service. He had decided to return to barnstorming and was offered a job with a group of aerial stuntmen called the Flying Circus at Denver, Colorado.

He traveled to Denver by train to meet his new employer, Captain J. Wray Vaughn. Vaughn had no idea what his new pilot looked like. He waited on the train station platform. The boyish young man with the bashful smile walked up to him. "Excuse me, sir. Are you Captain Vaughn?"

Vaughn said he was.

"I'm Lindbergh."

In utter surprise, Vaughn thought to himself, if this kid is a pilot, I'm a horse.

Lindy wasted no time in proving his skill. Later at the airport, Vaughn watched in amazement as the young pilot from Minnesota performed every trick in the stunt pilot's handbook.

Then to cap his performance Lindbergh climbed thousands of feet over the earth and put the plane into a screaming dive toward the ground.

Vaughn watched in growing horror. Surely the plane would crash! Already it had passed the point considered safe for recovery from a high dive. At the last possible moment Lindbergh pulled back on the control stick. Screaming like a wounded animal the plane swept out of the dive and climbed into the sky again. It seemed to Vaughn that the aircraft's wheels brushed tall grass on the field as it pulled out of the dive.

Vaughn was convinced. Later he said of Lindbergh, "There was never another like him."

Lindbergh continued barnstorming until 1926. By then he had gained a reputation as an expert pilot. The year before, the United States Congress had passed a bill granting privately owned companies the right to carry U.S. mail by air. Airmail service was first started in 1918, but the service had been operated by the U.S. Postal Department.

A company named the Robertson Corporation received a

contract to carry mail by air between St. Louis and Chicago. The company hired Lindbergh as its chief pilot. He chose two of his ex-military pilot friends to work with him. He set up the nine airfields where he was to deliver and pick up mail between St. Louis and Chicago, and the service began.

Only a well-trained, highly skilled pilot could fly the airmail service in the mid-twenties. Many of the flights were made at night. Over the years, Lindbergh had developed a wonderful sense of direction. There were many occasions when this ability proved invaluable, especially during night flights when the earth below was hidden beneath thick banks of fog.

Although the planes were modern and well-maintained, there were occasional mechanical failures. The pilots were forced to leap from their craft and parachute to the earth. Such falls were frightening enough in the daytime. At night, in a heavy fog, they could be terrifying.

By this time Lindbergh had become not only an expert pilot but a devoted aviator as well. Like hundreds before him, he strongly believed in the future of aviation. He knew if the airmail service were successful, it would greatly advance the cause of commercial aviation in the United States. One day, perhaps, the general public would stop thinking of the airplane as a toy, and of flying as a mere sport.

He wrote in *The Spirit of St. Louis,*

> We pilots of the mail have a tradition to establish. The commerce of the air depends on it. Men have already died for that tradition. Every division of the mail routes has its hallowed points of crash where some pilot on a stormy night, or lost and blinded by fog, laid down his life on the altar of his occupation.

The twenty-five-year-old pilot from the little farm town in Minnesota spoke from experience. Time and time again during his own flights between St. Louis and Chicago he was faced with "the altar of his occupation."

In his book Lindbergh told of one such occasion.

On a night flight to Chicago, the ground was hidden by fog as he neared his destination. The dense mist, 800 feet thick, completely obscured the landing field. Unable to find it, Lindbergh decided to fly back to the edge of the fog and land in a field. But the distance back was too great. His airplane had consumed all of its fuel.

With the few minutes' reserve fuel left in his tanks, Lindbergh brought his plane up to 5,000 feet and leaped over the side of the fuselage.

His parachute opened quickly, and he began the descent toward the blanket of fog far below.

Suddenly he heard the sound of an airplane. It was his own. A small amount of fuel left in the tanks had ignited the engine. And it was headed right at him!

"In spite of the sky's tremendous space, it seemed crowded with traffic," Lindbergh wrote. "I shoved my flashlight into my pocket and caught hold of the parachute risers [cords] so I could slip the canopy one way or the other in case the plane kept pointing toward me."

But the plane passed by, a hundred yards away. Breathing more easily he continued his descent into the fog. He braced himself for a landing in trees, or worse, on a barbed wire fence. Then he hit the ground. He had landed in a cornfield. The parachute collapsed and lay on top of the tall corn stalks.

Lindbergh gathered together the huge abundance of cloth and made his way out of the field. He found wagon tracks that led him to a farmyard. He was headed for the farmhouse when an automobile approached slowly, moving a spotlight from one side to another. He walked to the car and saw several people in it.

Lindbergh records the conversation that followed:

> "Did you hear that airplane?" one of them called out as I approached.
>
> "I'm the pilot," I said.
>
> "An airplane just dove into the ground," the man went on, paying no attention to my answer. "Must be right near here. Lord, it made a racket!" He kept searching with his spotlight, but the beam didn't show much in the haze.
>
> "I'm the pilot," I said again. "I was flying it." My words got through that time. The spotlight stopped moving.
>
> *"You're the pilot?* Good Lord, how——"
>
> "I jumped with a parachute," I said, showing him the white bundle.
>
> "You aren't hurt?"
>
> "Not a bit. But I've got to find the wreck and get the mail sacks."
>
> "It must be right near by. Get in and we'll drive along the road a piece. Good Lord, what went wrong? You must have had some experience! You're sure you aren't hurt?"

They spent a quarter of an hour searching, unsuccessfully. Then Lindbergh accompanied the farmer to his house and began to telephone other farms in the area. It took several hours for Lindbergh to reach a farmer who told him where the aircraft had struck the ground.

The plane was located about two miles from the house. Lindbergh and the farmer drove to the site of crash. The plane was a ball-shaped mass. It had narrowly missed a farmhouse, hooked one wing on a grain shock a quarter mile beyond, skidded along the ground for eighty yards, ripped through a fence, and come to rest on the edge of a cornfield. Splinters of wood and bits of torn fabric were strewn all around. The mail compartment was broken open and one sack had been thrown out. But the mail was undamaged, and Lindbergh took it to the nearest post office to be entrained. Then he returned by another train to St. Louis and in a few hours was in the air again, delivering more mail.

Yes, dangers were ever present. But there were also many flights in perfect weather. These are the great moments in a flier's life—when the night air is crystal clear and stars fill the skies and the air and the wind are at rest. He is alone with the earth and the sky. These are the moments when the flier thinks about his purpose in life, about his success or failure as a human being. These are the moments when he dreams great dreams.

It was on such a night in late 1926 that Chief Air Mail Pilot Charles Lindbergh was flying from Springfield, Illinois, to Chicago. It was a night of serene beauty, the kind of night that the true flier wishes would never end.

Lindbergh began thinking to himself:

> Why return to [earth]; why submerge myself in brick-walled human problems when all the crystal universe is mine? Like the moon, I can fly on forever through space, past the mail field in Chicago, beyond the state of Illinois, over mountains, over oceans, independent of the world below. . . .
>
> I grow conscious of the limits of my biplane, of the inefficiency of its wings, struts, and wires. They bind me to earth and to the field ahead at Chicago. A Bellanca [a new, fast airplane] would cruise at least fifteen miles an hour faster, burn only half the amount of gasoline, and carry

double the payload. . . . What a future aviation has when such planes can be built; yet how few people realize it! Businessmen think of aviation in terms of barnstorming, flying circuses, crashes, and high costs per flying hour. Somehow they must be made to understand the possibilities of flight . . .

If I only had the Bellanca, I'd show St. Louis businessmen what modern aircraft could do; I'd take them to New York in eight or nine hours. They'd see how swiftly and safely passengers could fly. . . . In a Bellanca filled with fuel tanks I could fly on all night, like the moon. . . . Possibly—my mind is startled at its thought—I could fly nonstop between New York and Paris.

Thus, as Lindbergh records it in *The Spirit of St. Louis,* the idea was born. Lindbergh continued his flight through the beautiful night toward Chicago. The thought would not leave his mind. Why shouldn't he fly from New York to Paris?

Indeed, why not?

I'll do it, he decided. I'll fly to Paris!

And, as always, when Charles Lindbergh made up his mind to do something, he took action.

A non-stop flight between New York and Paris was not a new idea. In 1919 the famed English flying team of John Alcock and Arthur Brown had made a 1,936-mile-long transatlantic flight from Newfoundland to Ireland. That same year a French hotel owner had offered a $25,000 prize for the first non-stop 3,610-mile flight between New York and Paris.

The year of 1927 seemed to be the moment in time when this great flight was to be accomplished. Lindbergh was not alone in his desire to make the trip. Several American aviators, including the famed explorer, Commander Richard

Byrd, were also readying aircraft for this journey. Others in France were making similar preparations.

The other competitors planned on two- or three-man crews flying in multi-engined aircraft. They all enjoyed the backing of wealthy men, and money was no problem.

Lindbergh thought that a single-engine plane stood the best chance of making the trip. And the Bellanca, he decided, was the perfect plane. But unlike his rivals, to him money *was* a problem.

Commander Byrd's financial backer had provided $100,-000 for the trip. Lindbergh decided the entire trip, including the cost of a plane, could be made for not more than $15,000. He put up $2,000 of his own money and set about looking for the remainder from financial backers.

Most of the men he approached expressed amazement at the idea of making the journey in a single-engine craft. Wasn't a tri-motor much safer? Patiently, again and again, Lindbergh explained that a single-engine could carry much more fuel than a larger plane. Less could go wrong with it, too. A multi-engined plane might stay in the air a short while longer, but over the empty Atlantic Ocean what difference did a few extra minutes make?

But to attempt the journey alone! Impossible! The pilot would have to stay awake for forty hours straight! A crew of at least two men was required. No, it couldn't be done alone.

"Yes, it can," Lindbergh replied quietly. "I can do it."

His earnestness, his obvious sincerity plus his solid reputation as a responsible aviator finally won. A group of St. Louis businessmen advanced him the $13,000.

Elated, Lindbergh immediately tried to buy the only Bellanca in existence. But its owners, the Wright Aeronautical Company, refused to sell. Lindbergh approached the builder, Guiseppe Bellanca, who agreed to build another plane. But he insisted that his company name the crew. Lindbergh refused. If anyone was going to fly in Charles Lindbergh's plane to Paris, it would be Charles Lindbergh!

For the next few weeks he cast about anxiously for an aircraft manufacturer who would build the type of airplane he needed, for the price he could pay. He found what he wanted in San Diego, California—the Ryan Aircraft Company, a small manufacturer located in an ancient building beside a fish cannery on the waterfront. The building was not impressive, but the company's little airplanes had earned a good reputation.

They agreed to build the airplane Lindbergh wanted. When he arrived in San Diego he spent several hours with the company's executives, including Donald Hall, the company's design engineer. A fast friendship formed between the two men. They worked side by side for the next two months.

Numerous problems had to be solved. The biggest one was weight. The heavier the airplane, the less fuel it could carry. The New York-Paris flight was about 3,600 miles. They decided the plane must carry enough fuel for 4,000 miles, leaving a 400 mile reserve in case the plane wandered off course during the flight.

Days and weeks slipped by. The tension mounted. Every man at the factory, from Hall to the mechanics building the plane, could think of nothing else. At the end of the work day, instead of going home, many of the men in the factory kept working on the aircraft.

The tension grew even greater when news of the trips being planned by the other competitors for the $25,000 prize appeared in the newspapers.

Lindbergh groaned inwardly when he read of the progress

his rivals were making. Surely they would beat him! It did not seem possible that his airplane would be ready before one of his competitors made the flight.

He began to have doubts. Perhaps he ought to change his plans. No one had yet flown the Atlantic Ocean alone. Maybe he ought to forget the New York-Paris flight. He telegraphed his financial backers in St. Louis. "No," they replied. "We've come this far. Keep going."

They were counting on him. They trusted him completely. So did everyone connected with the flight, from a bank president in St. Louis to an airplane mechanic in San Diego. It was a large, beautifully coordinated team, working together toward a single goal.

Slowly the airplane began to take shape. The framework of the fuselage was completed. Then the wings. Then the tail sections. Then the fuel tanks and the engine.

The airplane carried no excess weight. Over and over, Hall and Lindbergh discussed the different pieces of equipment the plane would need to make the journey. Again and again Lindbergh rejected items that other pilots would never fly without, including navigation equipment. He decided to fly with a simple compass and to depend upon his uncanny sense of direction. He even chose not to carry a parachute. Elimination of that 20-pound weight meant more miles in the air.

He would have to plot the course of the flight over the empty ocean. How? He had no real experience in celestial navigation. His simple compass and sense of direction might keep him pointed in the proper direction, but how could he know whether or not a side wind was pushing the plane off course? It would be impossible to determine over water.

Luck was with him. After searching about, he found several maps used by sea-going ships to travel the oceans. He used these to lay out the course of his flight. He rejected the idea of studying celestial navigation and using a sextant in flight, because his hands would be forced to leave the plane's controls to use the sextant.

Then, in the last week of April, the final touches were added to the plane. The mechanics who had worked so long and so hard signed their names on a spar before the final fabric covering was applied. They were proud of their handiwork. They wanted their names to fly the ocean with Lindbergh.

The craft was taken to an airfield at the edge of San Diego and made ready for the first test flight.

Lindbergh stared at it in wonder. Only two months ago it had been simply an idea, a desire, an ambition. Then men's minds and hands joined together. Standing before him was the result—the *Spirit of St. Louis*. It did not seem possible.

He climbed into the enclosed cockpit. The engine was started. Slowly, methodically, he checked the few instruments he hadn't discarded to save weight. Then, down the runway into the wind—the *Spirit of St. Louis* leaped into the air.

It was everything he dreamed of. The machine lived beneath his hands.

There were still minor adjustments to be made, but in general the craft responded exactly the way Lindbergh and Hall had planned. The next two weeks passed quickly. More test flights were made, tuning the sleek, single-engine, high-winged monoplane to mechanical perfection.

Finally, by May 10, all was ready. The next step was to fly the plane to St. Louis and show it to the backers. Bidding good-bye to friends in San Diego, Lindbergh took to the air.

The beginning of an historic air journey. Charles Lindbergh, in his Spirit of St. Louis, takes off from a San Diego, California, airfield, headed toward St. Louis, then New York City, then Paris.

Eastward over barren deserts and rugged mountain ranges the little plane soared.

Then, with nothing but primitive Arizona wilderness below, the engine suddenly began to sputter and cough.

Would it fail? Would he be forced to crash land? Had all the work, the planning, the dreaming been for nothing?

For the next four hours the plane fought and coughed its way across the sky. Lindbergh waited in dread of that final, awful silence that meant the engine had stopped. But it never came. Finally, near noon, the sputtering quieted and the engine began to run smoothly.

Fourteen hours and twenty-five minutes after takeoff, the *Spirit of St. Louis* landed in the city after which it had been named. It was a record flight, the fastest man had ever traveled from the Pacific Coast to St. Louis.

After two days at St. Louis, Lindbergh again put his machine into the air and flew to New York. He was greeted by friends and newspaper reporters. The news of his record flight across the country had preceded him.

The next eight days passed tensely. Each moment Lindbergh expected to hear that one of his rivals had beaten him. Several already had tried. Some of them died in the attempt.

By this time Lindbergh had been singled out by the national spotlight. He was considered a dark horse in the transatlantic race. He was young. He was going to try the trip alone in an unknown kind of airplane. He was competing against older, more experienced aviators who would be flying more powerful aircraft and who were being backed by very rich men. He was "the little guy against the big guys" and already a hero.

He did not like the feeling. He was a flier, he told himself, nothing more. The $25,000 prize awaiting the winner of the race was not really important. It was the accomplishment and what it could mean to the world of aviation that was the real goal.

Landing in New York City, he spent the next few days checking and rechecking the *Spirit of St. Louis*. Almost grudgingly, because of the weight they added, he had supplied himself with a few necessities for survival in case the plane went into the water. These supplies included a small raft and flares. His only food was to be five sandwiches and a water canteen.

By May 16 he and the *Spirit of St. Louis* were ready. But then the flier's eternal enemy, the weather, had its say in the manner. Fog and storms shrouded the course to Paris. For the next three days Lindbergh chafed under the pressure. The only comforting thing was that his competitors were also delayed by the storm.

Then, on May 19, Lindbergh heard that the weather over the ocean was clearing. But it might take another day or two for his route to be completely open.

He decided to take the risk. His competitors would probably wait for completely clear weather. Now was the time!

Final preparations on the *Spirit of St. Louis* were made rapidly. He returned to his hotel that night, hoping for at least two hours' sleep. But sleep evaded him. He decided to rise and head for the field.

The plane had been waiting at New York City's Curtiss Field. The rules for the prize stipulated that the flight must originate from another place, Roosevelt Field.

Lindbergh and his friends arrived at Curtiss by 3:00 A.M. The weather was overcast and a light rain was falling. It was decided to haul the plane to Roosevelt Field by truck rather than fly it. Lindbergh ordered the move to be made. He described the scene in *The Spirit of St. Louis:*

> Mechanics tie the plane's tail skid to the back of a motor truck and wrap a tarpaulin around the engine. Reporters button up their raincoats. Men look out into the night and shake their heads. The truck starter grinds. My plane lurches backward through a depression in the ground. It looks awkward and clumsy. It appears completely incapable of flight—shrouded, lashed, and dripping. Escorted by motorcycle police, pressmen, aviators, and a handful of onlookers, the slow, wet trip begins.
>
> It's more like a funeral procession than the beginning of a flight to Paris.

The flight that opened the world of modern aviation had begun.

Less than three hours later, Lindbergh taxied the fuel-laden *Spirit of St. Louis* onto the runway. Until this moment neither he nor Hall had been absolutely sure the plane could leave the ground carrying its large fuel load. Their theories and mathematical calculations told them it would. But, as always, there remained only one way to make sure.

Lindbergh eased the throttle forward. Slowly the *Spirit of St. Louis* began moving down the runway, gaining speed steadily. Lindbergh gripped the control stick, concentrating with all his might on keeping the craft moving straight.

At the far end of the field a web of telephone poles waited. Halfway down the runway the plane still had not left the ground. Lindbergh pulled back the stick. Several times the wheels left the runway, then touched again. Faster and faster the little plane sped over the ground.

Then it was in the air, clearing the telephone wires by twenty feet. Soon the earth dropped far below. The little aircraft turned and struck out on the first leg of its trip to Paris.

Hours and miles passed quickly at first. The plane responded perfectly beneath its pilot's hand.

The *Spirit of St. Louis* "seems to form an extension of my own body," Lindbergh wrote in *The Spirit of St. Louis*, "ready to follow my wish as the hand follows the mind's desire—instinctively, without commanding."

By the third hour they were well over the Atlantic. Lindbergh turned to the task of navigation and checking his course.

Onward the *Spirit of St. Louis* droned. Time and distance melted behind Lindbergh.

Then a new enemy confronted the pilot—the desire to sleep. He had not slept for twenty-four hours before taking off. Now it began to catch up with him. His eyelids grew heavier with each new hour; his body seemed to become a separate part of him, something distant. Time and again he caught himself slipping into sleep.

In every way possible he fought off the effect of the endless droning of the engine, the empty, unending water below, the unearthly feeling of drifting in space. He would shake himself violently and stamp his feet or let cold air blow into his face through the cockpit window. Anything to stay awake!

At times he actually fell asleep briefly with his eyes open. But so close was spiritual and physical contact with his aircraft that any slight change in altitude brought him awake.

The battle continued into the twentieth and twenty-first hours of flight, and on. Then he had flown twenty-four hours —through a day and night. He hoped when the second day appeared he would have won the battle against sleep. But the struggle continued. He had no desire for food or drink —only sleep, and that he could not—he must not—surrender to.

Then, during the twenty-seventh hour, he looked to the ocean below. His eyes widened. Slowly a message penetrated his dulled mind.

There were boats down there! It was a small fishing fleet.

An electric charge of recognition drove all thought of sleep from his mind. He banked the *Spirit of St. Louis* into a circle and swept over the fleet. Most of the boats looked deserted. Then he saw a man looking up at him from a porthole. Lindbergh flew low over the boat. He pulled the throttle back to decrease the engine noise and shouted down. "Which way is Ireland?"

Oddly enough the man showed no sign of response. Lindbergh could not wait. He returned the plane to its original eastward course, hoping soon to gain sight of the Irish coast.

Barely an hour later the southern tip of Ireland lay beneath him. During the trip, storm clouds had forced him to make several changes in course. His compass had also been affected by a magnetic storm through which the plane passed. Yet when he first sighted land, he was just three miles from his intended course! It had been an astounding work of navigation.

Across Ireland and England he flew. The English Channel passed below. Then he was over France. The little aircraft turned and headed toward Paris.

Then, in the thirty-third hour of flight, the city of Paris lay below. Lindbergh looked down and saw a long string of lights—headlights of automobiles caught in a vast traffic jam that stretched from the heart of Paris to the airport. He

Section 1 | "All the News That's Fit to Print."

The New York Times.

THE WEATHER
Generally fair today and tomorrow; moderate to fresh southerly winds.
Temperature reports on Page 28.

Section 1

VOL. LXXVI....No. 25,329.　　•　•　•　　NEW YORK, SUNDAY, MAY 22, 1927.　　FIVE CENTS

LINDBERGH DOES IT! TO PARIS IN 33½ HOURS;
FLIES 1,000 MILES THROUGH SNOW AND SLEET;
CHEERING FRENCH CARRY HIM OFF FIELD

COULD HAVE GONE 500 MILES FARTHER

Gasoline for at Least That Much More Flew at Times From 10 Feet to 10,000 Feet Above Water.

ATE ONLY ONE AND A HALF OF HIS FIVE SANDWICHES

Fell Asleep at Times but Quickly Awoke—Glimpses of His Adventure in Brief Interview at the Embassy.

MAP OF LINDBERGH'S TRANSATLANTIC ROUTE, SHOWING THE SPEED OF HIS TRIP.

CROWD ROARS THUNDEROUS WELCOME

Breaks Through Lines of Soldiers and Police and Surging to Plane Lifts Weary Flier from His Cockpit

AVIATORS RESCUE HIM FROM FRENZIED MOB OF 25,000

Paris Boulevards Ring With Celebration After Day and Night Watch—American Flag Is Called For and Wildly Acclaimed.

LINDBERGH'S OWN STORY TOMORROW.

Captain Charles A. Lindbergh was too exhausted after his arrival in Paris last night to do more than indicate, as told below, his experiences during his flight. After he awakes today, he will narrate the full story of his remarkable exploit for readers of Monday's New York Times.

By CARLYLE MACDONALD

PARIS, Sunday, May 22.—Captain Lindbergh was discovered at the American Embassy at 2:30 o'clock this morning. Attired in a pair of Ambassador Herrick's pajamas, he sat on the edge of a bed and talked of his flight. At the last moment Ambassador Herrick had canceled the plans of the reception committee and, by unanimous consent, took the flier to the embassy in the Place d'Iena.

A staff of American doctors who had arrived at Le Bourget Field early to minister to an "exhausted" aviator found instead a bright-eyed, smiling youth who refused to be examined.

"Oh, don't bother; I am all right," he said.

"I'd like to have a bath and a glass of milk. I would feel better." Lindbergh replied when the Ambassador asked him what he would like to have.

A bath was drawn immediately and in less than five minutes the youth had disrobed in one of the embassy guest rooms, taken his bath and was out again drinking a bottle of milk and eating a roll.

"No Use Worrying," He Tells Envoy.

"There is no use worrying about me, Mr. Ambassador," Lindbergh insisted when Mr. Herrick and members of the embassy staff urged him to be examined by doctors and then go to bed immediately.

It was apparent that the young man was too full of his experiences to want sleep and he sat on the bed and chatted with the Ambassador, his son and daughter-in-law.

By this time a corps of frantic newspaper men who had been ready chasing the airman, following one false scent after another, had finally tracked him to the embassy. In a body they descended upon the Ambassador, who received them in the salon and informed them that he had just left Lindbergh with strict instructions to go to sleep.

As Mr. Herrick was talking with the reporters his son-in-law came downstairs and said that Lindbergh had rung and announced that he did not care to go to sleep yet and that he would be glad to see the newspaper men for a few minutes. A cheer went up from the group who dashed by Mr. Herrick and rushed upstairs.

Expected Trouble Over Newfoundland.

In the blue and gold room, with a soft light glowing, sat the conqueror of the Atlantic. He immediately stood up and held out his hands to greet his callers. THE NEW YORK TIMES correspondent being first to greet him.

"Sit down, please," urged every one with one voice, but Lindbergh only smiled again his famous boyish smile and said with brief, nonchalant answers.

"I expected trouble over Newfoundland because I had been warned that the situation there was unfavorable. But I got over that hazard with no trouble whatsoever."

"However, it wasn't easy going. I had sleet and snow for over 1,000 miles. Sometimes it was too high to fly over and sometimes too low to fly under, so I just had to go through it as best I could.

"I flew as low as 10 feet in some places and as high as 10,000 in others. I passed no ships in the daytime, but at night I saw the lights of several ships, the night being bright and clear."

Everyone then wanted to know if the flier had been asleep on the voyage.

"I didn't really get what you might call downright sleepy," he said, "but I think I sort of nodded several times. In fact, I could have flown half that distance again. I had enough fuel

Continued on Page Two.

LEVINE ABANDONS BELLANCA FLIGHT

Venture Given Up as Designer Splits With Him—Plane Narrowly Escapes Burning.

BYRD'S CRAFT IS NAMED

Lindbergh Cheered at Ceremony—Commander, Now Last in Field, Waits on Weather.

Through no fault of his own, Clarence D. Chamberlin, who with Bert Acosta established a world's non-stop flying record a few weeks ago, will not fly the much-heralded Bellanca monoplane in an attempt to establish a second New York-Paris non-stop flight.

G. M. Bellanca, designer of the plane, and Charles E. Levine of the Columbia Aircraft Company, owner of the ship, came to the parting of the ways last night and the project finally severed his connection with the promoter. Then Levine issued a statement that the prospect flight, which has been talked of for weeks, was off.

The statement said:

"Due to the crowning blow of Mr. Bellanca's resignation, I am forced to be placed in the hangar. Mr. Bellanca's resignation means to our abandon the plans for the New York-Paris flight for the present."

At the very moment that the statement was issued the plane was near the runway at Roosevelt Field with gas tanks filled and oil and equipment aboard ready for the start for Paris.

A few minutes later, as it was being wheeled off, preparatory to being housed for the night, it narrowly escaped being destroyed by fire. When the word came to the field that the flight was definitely off mechanics were ordered to empty one gasoline tank to lighten the machine. The gasoline spilled on the ground and while the ship was being towed away a careless spectator threw the stub of a lighted cigarette down.

In an instant there was a terrific flare and a dense burst of smoke as the gasoline blazed up.

"The Bellanca's gone," was the cry that rose from thousands of spectators who had gathered at the field.

Word was flashed to the army air station at Mitchel Field that there had been an accident and ambulance and fire-fighting apparatus were sent across the field. An ambulance from the Nassau County Hospital at Mineola was also sent to Roosevelt Field, as well as fire apparatus from Mineola.

The plane, however, was beyond the danger line and was not injured.

It had been announced that the Columbia would take off at 6 o'clock and Chamberlin was in his flying clothes ready to climb into the cockpit with the motored pilot who was to have accompanied him on the voyage.

With the elimination of the Bellanca monoplane, only Lieut.

Continued on Page Ten.

Times Wide World Photos.

CAPTAIN CHARLES A. LINDBERGH,
Who Flew Alone Across the Atlantic From New York to Paris, in Thirty-three and One-half Hours.

New York Stages Big Celebration After Hours of Anxious Waiting

Harbor Craft, Factories, Fire Sirens and Radio Carry Message of the Flier's Victory Throughout the City—Theatres Halt While Audiences Cheer.

New York bubbled all day yesterday with excitement and expectancy, first yearning for word of Captain Lindbergh, then half-doubting, gaily confident as the afternoon progressed and finally acclaiming the victory of the young aviator. In several conversations when the crowds were thickest, in which the ancient phrase, "I tell you so," was often repeated. It was evident during the day that New York had confidence in the lad from the West.

On the streets and elsewhere Lindbergh was the one topic of conversation the whole day long. In the subway, on the elevated, in trains and cars, in office buildings, theatres, wherever a few had gathered, or even where one man could find another to talk to, conversation always ran to "Lindbergh — Lindbergh."

And such expressions as this:

"He'll make it, all right."

"Some baby!"

"Well, if he's hit Ireland, he's safe anyway."

"He's away ahead of his time."

"What's the difference in time between here and there, anyway?"

Continued On Page Three.

She said it with an air which significant, first "I don't care maybe." surprising number of persons indicated that the difference in time was three hours.

Early in the day, even before there was any good reason why there should be definite news, the interest of the people was demonstrated in two ways. At every news stand there were little groups scanning the headlines and buying newspapers. In every newspaper office the switchboards were literally swamped with inquiries. It was not sufficient that any one, or later, that Lindbergh's plane had been seen over Ireland. The inquirers wanted specific information:

"Well, when will you get the first news?" they asked. And later:

"If he's over Ireland how long will it be before he gets to Paris?"

"Is he all right?"

The questions that were asked, considering that no news could possibly come direct from Captain Lindbergh unless he landed, were as astonishing as the guesses at the difference in time.

The Times Gets 10,000 Phone Calls.

The telephone inquiries came from all sorts of people and all directions. They covered all sorts of questions and were surprisingly explicit that they were an aid links or chambers at a distance, and hence could not

Continued on Page Three.

LINDBERGH TRIUMPH THRILLS COOLIDGE

President Cables Praise to "Heroic Flier" and Concern for Nungesser and Coli.

CAPITAL THROBS WITH JOY

Kellogg, New, MacNider, Patrick and Many More Join in Paying Tribute to Daring Youth.

Special to The New York Times.

WASHINGTON, May 21.—The triumph of Captain Charles A. Lindbergh in flying from New York to Paris without a stop created a tremendous emotion in the national capital and found immediate response in a host of official messages and statements congratulating the daring aviator upon his achievement. President Coolidge expressed his admiration in a message transmitted through Ambassador Herrick in Paris for delivery to the young flier in person.

With a single possible exception, this city has never been more thrilled since the armistice, when Woodrow Wilson mingled with surging thousands in celebrating the end of the war. The exception was when Walter Johnson arose from apparent defeat and won the deciding world series baseball game in 1924.

"The American people," the President said, "rejoice with me at the brilliant termination of your heroic flight. The first non-stop flight of a lone aviator across the Atlantic crowns the record of American aviation and is bringing of the greetings of the American people to France you likewise carry the assurance of our admiration of those intrepid Frenchmen, Nungesser and Coli, whose bold spirits first ventured on your exploit, and likewise a message of our continued anxiety concerning their fate."

Secretary Kellogg, in a message similarly transmitted, said:

"I heartily congratulate you on your good reason why their navigating a non-stop flight from New York to Paris. It is a great step to the advancement of aviation. Every one in the United States is proud of your accomplishment."

Kerr Lindbergh as a Boy.

In a statement issued here Mr. Kellogg referred to his personal friendship for Lindbergh, whom he has known for years through the young man's late father, a Representative in Congress from the Sixth District of Minnesota.

"News has just reached me," Mr. Kellogg said, "of the success of Lindbergh in completing his flight from New York to Paris. It is an achievement of which every American can justly be proud. I knew Lindbergh when he was a boy and rejoice at this culmination of his ambitions, which would only have been gained by a cool, courageous, superb courage and physique and sterling character. Our experience of Lindbergh's success, however, is tempered by our continued anxiety over the fate of Nungesser and Coli, whose courage and valor lure an equally warm place in our hearts."

Secretary of War Davis said:

"Words fail me to express...

Continued on Page Seven.

LINDBERGH TRIUMPH THRILLS COOLIDGE

By EDWIN L. JAMES.

Copyright, 1927, by The New York Times Company.
Special Cable to THE NEW YORK TIMES.

PARIS, May 21.—Lindbergh did it. Twenty minutes after 10 o'clock tonight suddenly and softly there slipped out of the darkness a gray-white airplane as 25,000 pairs of eyes strained toward it. At 10:24 the Spirit of St. Louis landed and thousands of soldiers, ranks of policemen and stout steel fences went down before a mad rush as irresistible as the tides of the ocean.

"Well, I made it," smiled Lindbergh, as the little white monoplane came to a halt in the middle of the field and the French vanguard reached the plane. Lindbergh made a move to jump out. Twenty hands reached for him and lifted him out as if he were a baby. Several thousands in a minute were around the plane. Thousands more broke the barriers of iron rails round the field, cheering wildly.

Lifted From His Cockpit.

As he was lifted to the ground Lindbergh was pale, and, with his hair tousled, he looked completely worn out. He had strength enough, however, to smile, and waved his hand to the crowd. Soldiers with fixed bayonets made in vain to keep back the crowd.

United States Ambassador Herrick was among the first to welcome and congratulate the hero.

A NEW YORK TIMES man was one of the first to reach the machine after its graceful descent to the field. These first to arrive at the plane had a picture that will live in their minds for the rest of their lives. His cap off, his tousled locks falling in disarray around his eyes, "Lucky Lindy" sat peering out over the rim of the little cockpit of his machine.

Dramatic Scene at the Field.

It was high drama. Picture the scene. Twenty to twenty-five thousand people were massed on the east side of Le Bourget air field. Some of them had been there six and seven hours. Off to the left the giant photo lighthouse of Mount Valérien flashed its guiding light 300 miles into the air. Closer on the left Le Bourget Lighthouse twinkled, and off to the right another giant revolving glare sent its beams high into the heavens.

Big are lights on all sides with enormous electric glares were flooding the landing field. From time to time rockets rose and burst in varied lights over the field.

Seven thirty, the hour announced for the arrival, had come and gone. Then 8 o'clock came, and no Lindbergh; at 9 o'clock the sun had set but then came reports that Lindbergh had been seen over Cork. Then he had been seen over Valentia in Ireland and then over Plymouth.

Suddenly a message spread like lightning, the aviator had been seen over Cherbourg. However, remembering the messages telling of Captain Nungesser's flight, the crowd was skeptical.

"One chance in a thousand!" "Oh, he cannot do it without navigating instruments!" "It's a pity, because he was a brave boy." Pessimism had spread over the great throng by 10 o'clock.

The stars came out and a chill wind high...

Watchers Are View Disappointed.

Suddenly the field lights flooded their glares onto the landing ground and there came the roar of an airplane's motor. The crowd was still, then began a cheer, but two minutes later the landing glares went dark for the searchlight had identified the plane and it was not Captain Lindbergh's.

Stamping their feet in the cold, the crowd waited patiently. It seemed quite apparent that many every one of them would be wait all night, hoping against hope.

Suddenly—it was 10:16 exactly—another motor roared over the heads of the crowd. In the sky one caught a glimpse of a white gray plane, and for an instant heard the sound of the motor. Then it dimmed, and the idea spread that it was just another disappointment.

Again landing lights glared and almost by the time they had flooded the field the gray-white plane had lighted on the far side nearly half a mile from the crowd. It rushed to stop almost at the far end, so gently did it land.

And then occurred a scene which almost beand description. Two companies of soldiers with fixed bayonets and the Le Bourget field police, reinforced by Paris agents, had held the crowd in good order. But as the plane showed the p...

44ᵉ Année — N° 15766
ÉDITION DE 5 HEURES
Dimanche 22 Mai 1927

LA TEMPÉRATURE

Le Matin

5 H   5 H   25c
SEUL A PARIS PRINCIPALEMENT, PARIS 183 RUES DES ITALIENS   MATIN-PARIS TÉL. : PROVENCE 19-01, 15-02, 15-03, 15-04

" ... Il faut prêcher,
non la lutte de classes,
mais la guerre de races."
(INSTRUCTION SECRÈTE DES SOVIETS
A LEURS AGENTS EN TURQUIE.)

L'ADMIRABLE EXPLOIT AÉRIEN EST RÉALISÉ

LE "MATIN" AUX ÉTATS-UNIS

L'aviateur américain Lindbergh a traversé l'Atlantique

DE NEW-YORK A PARIS SANS ESCALE, SEUL SUR SON AVION

Il a atterri hier soir au Bourget, à 22 h. 22, après avoir survolé l'Irlande, l'Angleterre, la Manche et la Normandie

Il franchit les 6.000 kilomètres du parcours en 33 heures 30 à la moyenne horaire de 179 kilomètres

Une foule de cent mille spectateurs l'acclame à l'atterrissage au Bourget

EXTÉNUÉ, L'AVIATEUR EUT CEPENDANT LA FORCE DE SOURIRE

L'ENTHOUSIASME A PARIS

IL EST ALLÉ SALUER LE SOLDAT INCONNU

Charles LINDBERGH

L'ARRIVÉE AU BOURGET

SUR LES BOULEVARDS

LINDBERGH A BATTU
le record du monde
en ligne droite sans escale

Départ : 20 mai, 12 h. 52
Arrivée : 21 mai, 22 h. 22
Distance : 6.000 kilomètres
Durée : 33 heures 30
Moyenne horaire : 179 kilomètres

VOIR EN DERNIÈRE HEURE
LE RÉCIT ÉMOUVANT DE DEUX
TÉMOINS MILITAIRES

La propagande soviétique à l'œuvre

DE REGRETTABLES INCIDENTS
au 105ᵉ régiment d'artillerie
lourde à Bourges

M. MELLON

Les idées directrices
de M. Mellon

Par Jules SAUERWEIN

A l'arrivée au Bourget, on protège l'avion contre la foule

LE RÉCIT DU RAID PAR L'AVIATEUR CHARLES LINDBERGH SERA PUBLIÉ PAR LE "MATIN"

Le "Matin" s'est assuré l'exclusivité en France de la publication du récit par l'aviateur
Charles Lindbergh de son inoubliable traversée aérienne de l'Atlantique de New-York à Paris.
Le compte rendu de cette émouvante randonnée commencera incessamment.

didn't realize this was part of his reception committee.

Lindbergh banked over the field and circled for landing. Gracefully the *Spirit of St. Louis* dropped onto French soil.

The first non-stop transatlantic flight was over.

Lindbergh had never really imagined what his reception at Paris's Le Bourget airport would be like. He could never have guessed.

The world went mad.

The *Spirit of St. Louis* had been sighted over Ireland and England and as it made its way toward Paris. Word of its arrival had flashed ahead. When Lindbergh stepped out of the cockpit, fifty thousand Frenchmen greeted him with great roaring approval. Pressing around the young pilot and his little aircraft, they raised him to their shoulders and paraded him jubilantly around the field.

From that moment on, Lindbergh's life was never the same. He was catapulted into fame. Kings gave banquets in his honor. President Calvin Coolidge awarded him the Congressional Medal of Honor. Messages from heads of government around the world were sent to him. Cities and nations honored him.

He had become "the Lone Eagle."

But perhaps the reward he regarded most highly was the world's awakening to the great potential of aviation. His solitary journey achieved the desired affect. Commercial airlines in the United States suddenly blossomed and grew. Aviation, at last, was accepted as an everyday thing.

At this moment, as you read these words, there are thousands of people in gigantic luxury airliners skimming across the sky. Some are flying for pleasure, some for business. They travel in the most modern aircraft that technology can develop, some at speeds above that of sound.

It all began with the *Spirit of St. Louis* and a brave young man whose great courage helped him achieve a dream.

Truly, Charles Lindbergh was master of the sky.

The Flight of Freedom Seven

THE AIRPORT MANAGER smiled at the teenage boy
in front of him. They stood in the manager's office at one
corner of the huge airplane hangar. Outside the door, several small aircraft were positioned at random across the
broad concrete floor. Through tall wide doors at each end
of the building came the sound of other planes taking off
and landing on the nearby airfield.

"So you're interested in flying?" the manager said.

"Yes sir," the youth replied. "I'll be happy to do odd jobs
for you around the hangar. For payment, I'd just like to go
up in a plane with one of the pilots."

"Where do you live?" the manager asked.

"In East Derry."

"East Derry? That's ten miles away. How did you get
here?" The boy didn't look old enough to drive an automobile.

"On my bicycle."

The manager's eyes widened. "Bicycle? You mean to say
you're willing to pedal your bike ten miles here and ten miles

back just so you can work a few hours to get a plane ride now and then?"

"Yes sir," the youth answered seriously.

The manager laughed. There was admiration in his voice.

"Well, if flying means that much to you, I guess we can work out a deal. Start right now if you want to. Grab a broom and sweep the hangar floor. Later we'll work out how much flying time you can have for each hour you work. All right?"

"You bet!" the youth replied happily. He turned and left the office. The manager watched as the young man found a broom and began to sweep the concrete floor energetically. The boy and his broom looked very small in the immense interior of the hangar.

Still smiling, the manager returned to his work. Now that's what I call determination, he said to himself. It's sure a pleasure to meet a boy who is willing to work for something he wants. That's the kind you hear about when they grow up.

Soon the boy made his first airplane flight. There, high above the earth, he felt the great thrill of freedom that every aviator from Pilatre de Rozier to Charles Lindbergh had experienced. That boy's first flight was the beginning of a brilliant career as an aviator.

The airport manager had been correct. The boy *was* the kind you "hear about" when they grew up. On May 5, 1961, he made an aerial journey that gave 150 million Americans a greater and stronger pride in their country.

His occupation—astronaut.

His journey—the first American voyage into outer space.

His name—Alan Bartlett Shepard, Jr.

The world of aviation had fully matured by the 1950's. Since the flight of the *Spirit of St. Louis* in 1927, aviation had grown with each passing day. Larger, more powerful airplanes were sent aloft. Then the jet airplane made its first appearance.

Time and distance between the cities of the world continued to shrink. Lindbergh's trip from New York to Paris took 33½ hours in 1927. By 1958 giant airliners made the same journey in just a few hours. Airplanes in the sky became as common as ships in the sea.

Man had truly mastered the sky, and still he was not satisfied. Now he looked beyond the sky. He fixed his eyes upon the stars.

The pioneers were still among us. They had changed only a little. They dressed differently from Joseph and Etienne Montgolfier. Their educations were more complete than the Wright brothers'. Electronic computers and slide rules had replaced long-hand mathematics.

But the urge was the same, the urge to challenge a new frontier—the stars.

The pioneers set to work. They developed great rockets that traveled thousands of miles at great speeds. They sent small containers called satellites into orbit around the earth. They shot un-piloted vehicles millions of miles into space to send back information on the other planets in our solar system. Then the first passengers—mice, dogs, chimpanzees— hurtled into orbit and returned to earth.

Finally, in 1960, man prepared to put himself into outer space.

Onto this dramatic stage in the history of aviation stepped Alan Shepard.

Alan was born in 1923 in East Derry, New Hampshire. His father, an insurance broker, was a retired Army colonel.

As Alan grew up it became apparent that he loved a challenge. He enjoyed the thrill of facing a problem and solving it. It made no difference whether the problem was mental or physical. Solving it successfully and completely was all that mattered.

He also knew that if he wanted something badly enough, he had to work for it. This was why he was willing to ride his bicycle twenty miles and work in the airport hangar just to get an occasional airplane ride.

Early in life Alan decided upon a military career. He attended the United States Naval Academy at Annapolis, Maryland, and was graduated in 1944. He spent the last few months of World War II on a Navy destroyer in the Pacific. Then he took military flight training and became a naval aviator.

The years between the end of the war and 1959 were busy for Alan. By 1950 he was a tremendously skilled aviator. He became a Navy test pilot and helped to develop modern types of Navy jet airplanes.

The work of a test pilot demands that a man keep in the best possible physical and mental condition. His reflexes must be perfect. His life depends upon how quickly he can deal with an emergency. He must be able to recognize a problem and come up with the answer instantly.

This was why Alan Shepard was such an expert aviator. Mastering a problem was his way of life.

Sometimes the challenges were physical. His plane's engine might quit suddenly. He had to discover what was wrong quickly and correct it. Other times the challenges were mental. During his years as a Navy pilot Alan confronted personal fear often.

One night he was in the air returning to his aircraft carrier, which was cruising near the coast of Korea. The weather was poor. The ocean below lay hidden by a thick cover of

U. S. Navy Commander Alan B. Shepard, America's first man in space.
Years of experience made Shepard an expert pilot, one reason why he
was chosen to be among America's first astronauts.

clouds, and the aircraft's electronic navigation instruments
weren't functioning properly.

Shepard began to taste fear. You're in trouble, he thought.
The plane's fuel is running low. The radio aids aren't working right. You might have to ditch the plane in the ocean.

The fear grew stronger. If he ditched, how would the carrier be able to rescue him? By the time the ship reached the
place his plane had crashed, he might have drifted miles away.

And the water. It was ice cold. He'd heard many stories
about pilots who had crashed and caught pneumonia and
died before they were ever found.

Now wait a minute, Shepard commanded himself. This
kind of thinking isn't getting you anywhere. All right, so
you're in trouble. How do you get out of it? Be calm. The
plane is still flying. Use all your years of training. You can

find the carrier if you try hard enough. Shut out the fear. That's your worst enemy right now. Forget that you're afraid. Concentrate. Concentrate.

A short while later, Alan found the carrier and landed safely. Fear had challenged him and he had mastered it.

In 1958 the United States space agency, the National Aeronautics and Space Administration, announced it was looking for experienced military aviators to train as the nation's first astronauts. Alan was immediately interested.

He didn't need to apply for the program. His reputation, his experience and his abilities were well known. He was one of the best. He knew it and so did NASA. A few months after the announcement, he was asked to discuss with NASA the possibility of joining the space program.

The idea delighted Shepard. Over the years he had become the complete aviator, and he realized that aviation now had reached a new stage in its growth. The new frontier was outer space. And Alan Shepard wanted to be one of the first to challenge the unknowns that lay ahead.

"It would give me a chance to be not just a pilot, but a *space* pilot, and to get in on the ground floor of something new and important," Shepard recalled in *We Seven*, an account of the Mercury space program written by the nation's first astronauts.

"I guess everyone feels an urge to do something no one else has ever done—the urge to pioneer and to accept a challenge and then try to meet it. I realized what it [the U.S. space program] would mean to the nation in prestige and morale. And I felt that I would like to contribute whatever ability and maturity I had achieved. . . . But the tests we had to take were not exactly easy, and I was not sure that I had made the team."

The tests *were* tough. The men chosen to be the first
United States astronauts had to be good. NASA wanted men
whose training and background would enable them to master the complicated controls of a space vehicle. "What we're
looking for," said an Air Force general in jest, "is a group of
ordinary supermen."

After a period of numerous physical and psychological
tests, a long, tense wait followed. From a total of 508 test
pilots, the number was reduced to 110. Then it dropped to
69, then 32, and down to 18.

Finally, on April 9, 1959, the final seven men—the first
American astronauts—were introduced to the nation.
Among the seven was U.S. Navy Commander Alan Shepard.
He had made it. But that was only the beginning.

During the next two years a great project was formed—
Project Mercury. Its goal was to send a man into orbit around
the earth. The entire program had to be planned step by
step, measure by measure.

For the next two years Shepard and his fellow astronauts
devoted every ounce of energy to Project Mercury. They
were all expert pilots and engineers. But even this experience
wasn't enough. As a baby must learn to walk, Shepard and
the other astronauts had to learn how to fly in outer space.
It had never been done before. They had to learn from the
beginning.

It wasn't easy. It meant much study. For months they
studied the results of experimental flights. Alan spent
hours in a model of the Mercury space capsule rehearsing
every part of the flight. At the same time he had to work hard
at different exercises to keep himself in the excellent physical
condition that NASA required of the astronauts.

Working together, side by side, day by day, the seven

astronauts became a closely knit team. They came to know each other's mannerisms and moods. They all developed a real fondness and a sincere respect for each other. One of them once said, "The Navy lost a good officer when Al [Shepard] came into the program. He takes the admiral's big-picture view of the fleet. He feeds all the little items into place and is not confused by the details. Once he sets himself to an argument, he's tough . . . and usually right."

The months passed. Constant refinements were made on the space capsule. It was to be a small vehicle. Its pilot would

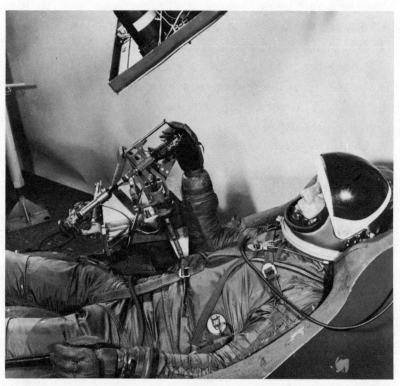

NASA

Training for the flight of Freedom Seven **included long, tedious hours of practice in a replica of the space capsule's cabin.**

barely have room to move. The many instruments, levers and switches had to be in the most convenient positions on the instrument panel in front of him, and he had to master them.

The flight rehearsals continued. Shepard and his six companions passed hours learning how to escape from the capsule if it were to land in water or on land. They also spent many hours flying as passengers in large empty cargo planes with padded walls. The plane would maneuver in a way that would make the astronauts weightless for a short time. They grew accustomed to the weightlessness they would experience in outer space away from the force of gravity.

Other long hard hours were spent in a centrifuge machine. This strange-looking device was constructed with a 50-foot-long arm. At the end of the arm was a sealed gondola.

The astronaut would seat himself in the gondola. The arm would begin to revolve faster and faster. As the speed increased, the astronauts would feel the pressure of "G-force." One "G" is equal to the normal weight of a person.

Shepard's average weight was 165 pounds. As the speed of the centrifuge increased, he would feel the pressure of two G's, meaning that he actually weighed twice his normal weight—330 pounds. It was not unusual for the centrifuge to exert as many as eight G's on the astronaut, which meant that he might weigh 1,300 pounds.

Gradually the problems were solved, and the day approached when the first manned flight would be made.

The first flight would be "sub-orbital." The Mercury space capsule would be shot from Cape Canaveral (now Cape Kennedy), Florida, in a bullet-like path into space and then down into the Atlantic Ocean. It would not go into orbit. The date of the first sub-orbital flight had not yet been selected, although it was expected to take place in the spring of 1961.

None of the seven astronauts yet knew which of them would be selected by NASA to make the first flight. They all wanted to go. But being "first" was not nearly as important as continuing work together to bring the Mercury program to its fulfillment. They continued working as a team, never letting their individual desires to be first interfere with their work.

Then NASA announced that one of three men would be the first American into space—John Glenn, Virgil Grissom, or Alan Shepard. Several more weeks would pass before the final choice would be announced.

The day of the first flight approached. The entire nation watched Cape Canaveral, where the final preparations were being made.

But then, on April 12, 1961, a great historical flight took place. Soviet Russia put the first man into space. The name of the Russian cosmonaut was Yuri Gagarin. He made a complete orbit around the earth before landing. His flight surprised the entire world. The Russians had kept their plans for the flight in complete secrecy. Not until the cosmonaut was already in space did his country announce the great feat.

The Russians have done it first! This thought occurred to every American. The United States had hoped it could be the first into space. But the Russians had done it before us, just as they had in 1957 by launching the first earth satellite into orbit.

But the U.S. did not allow the Russian success to stop or slow down the Mercury program. And among the many determined men who doubled their efforts were the seven astronauts.

Several weeks after Gagarin's flight, the announcement was made: The United States would make its first manned sub-orbital flight on May 2, 1961. As yet, the pilot still had not been chosen.

Then, word came that the seven astronauts were to report to the office of Robert Gilruth, director of NASA's Space Task Group. The seven men entered the office. Gilruth was waiting for them.

"Commander Shepard will be the pilot," he announced simply. "John Glenn will be back-up pilot."

Shepard said nothing for a moment and kept his eyes on the floor. Then he looked up.

"Everyone in the room was staring at me," he wrote in *We Seven*. "I was excited and happy, of course. But it was not a moment to crow. Each of the other fellows had very much wanted to be first himself. And now, after almost two years of hard work and training, that chance was gone.

"Then the others, with grins on their faces covering up what must have been their own great disappointment, came over and congratulated me."

He was to be first! It had not seemed possible to him. But it was. And now he must work even harder. He must concentrate all his thoughts and energy on the task that lay ahead. During the next six weeks he went through forty stimulated flight tests, rehearsing his duties during the upcoming flight over and over again.

There was to be a great difference between the American and Russian space flights. The Russians had veiled their space efforts with secrecy. Only after success was assured did

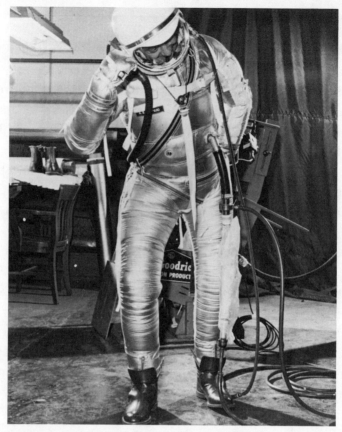

NASA

**Commander Shepard tries on the spacesuit he will wear
during his flight. Each spacesuit is tailor-made for the astronaut who will wear it.**

they announce the project. In contrast, the United States
allowed the entire world to look over its shoulder as it prepared to go into space. If a mistake was made, the world
would know about it immediately.

And so, on May 2, 1961, the prestige of the entire United
States rested on the shoulders of Alan Shepard as he prepared
for the flight at Cape Canaveral. Everything seemed ready.
He awakened at 1:00 A.M., ate breakfast, and then submitted
to the final physical tests. Electronic sensing devices were

positioned on his body. These would send radio signals back to earth telling medical observers how his body functioned during the flight. Then he donned his silver space suit. His space helmet was lowered over his head and clamped in place.

At 5:00 A.M. he was ready to be taken to the launching pad.

But then word came: The mission had to be cancelled. Thick storm clouds hung over Cape Canaveral. It would be too risky to attempt the launching. It meant that the long countdown, the time it took to fuel the missile and give it a final checking over, would have to be repeated. It meant a delay of at least two more days. Alan removed his space suit and returned to work.

With stubborn determination, NASA repeated the entire countdown procedure.

On the morning of May 5, Shepard left the building where he had once again submitted to physical examinations and donned his space suit.

MR-3—*Freedom Seven*—awaited him. It stood tall and graceful in the center of Launch Pad 5. A huge gantry crane stood alongside. Alan calmly entered the crane's elevator and rode to its top. Carefully he climbed into the instrument-crowded interior of *Freedom Seven*. The launch crew bolted the hatch over him.

Everything seemed ready.

But was it?

A heavy cloud cover still lay over the Cape. The NASA weather experts decided the launching must wait for a hole in the clouds.

The hole finally appeared. It looked as though the ancient foe—the weather—had relented. But then another difficulty developed. A minor mechanical trouble had to be repaired.

The minutes ticked by slowly. The countdown was resumed, nearly four hours after Alan had entered the capsule.

Then, at "T" (time of launch) minus two minutes and forty seconds, the fourth "hold" of the morning was announced. A problem had developed in the missile's fuel system.

Alan lay in the capsule and listened to the voices of the engineers in his earphones. They were discussing the new problem and wondering if the launch should, after all, be canceled. It was obvious that their concern was primarily for the astronaut.

Alan became impatient. "I'm cooler than you are," he said into his microphone. "Why don't you fix your little problem and light this candle?"

They set to work and repaired the problem. The countdown began again.

Across the United States, millions of Americans waited, hypnotized by the events taking place on the sandy Florida beach called Cape Canaveral. People sat silently before radios and before television receivers as the countdown continued. Business establishments hooked radios to loudspeaker systems so that office workers could listen to the launch. Teachers in thousands of schools allowed their students to listen to the radio broadcast in their classrooms and study halls. Alan Shepard sat alone in *Freedom Seven*. But with him were the prayers of millions of his fellow Americans.

The countdown reached "one." And then:

"Ignition!"

A great orange flame burst from beneath the base of the rocket. The nation held its breath.

Cleanly, without tremor or hesitation, the missile lifted

On the morning of May 5, 1961, amidst a thundering roar and great blast of flame, Freedom Seven and its human passenger were lifted from the launch pad by powerful Redstone rockets and hurled into space.

itself from the concrete launch pad. A spear of white-hot flame blazed from its tail. Then the spear changed to a yellow ball of fire.

The thunderous roar from the missile echoed across Cape Canaveral. Higher and higher the space ship lifted.

Alan's voice crackled over the radio. "Roger, lift-off and the clock is started!"

"Reading you loud and clear," said NASA.

"This is *Freedom Seven*," replied Shepard. "The fuel is 'Go'. One-point-two G. Cabin at 14 psi. Oxygen is 'Go'."

The missile shrank into a small speck in the sky. Then a cloud of smoke burst behind it. The rocket had separated from the capsule.

An American was in space. Pride and relief swept over the millions listening to the radio broadcasts or watching the launch on television—pride in their nation, relief for Alan Shepard.

The flight continued for the next fifteen minutes. Shepard performed his various duties coolly and confidently. The nation listened to his calm voice and admired his courage.

"What a beautiful view!" he exclaimed a few minutes after his journey began. He had just looked out *Freedom Seven*'s periscope and seen the brilliant blues and greens and whites of the earth below him.

But he was too busy to admire the view for long. The flight neared its end. He had to position the capsule for re-entry into the earth's atmosphere.

It was a dangerous moment. If he re-entered at too steep an angle, the friction of the atmosphere against the outer surface of *Freedom Seven* would burn the ship and its pilot to a crisp. Carefully Alan put the capsule into the proper position, just as he had rehearsed so many times on earth.

Astronaut Shepard

During the long plunge back toward earth, he experienced the pressure of eleven G's—his weight actually increased to more than 1,800 pounds.

"Okay, okay, okay," he kept repeating, grunting the word with effort. He wanted to show the NASA Control Center that he was still well in spite of the huge "G" force.

Again the nation held its breath as the space ship hurtled toward the ocean below.

At 9:49, automatically operated parachutes dropped *Freedom Seven* into the Atlantic. The trip had lasted only fifteen minutes. During that time *Freedom Seven* reached a speed of 5,200 miles an hour and gained a height of 116 miles over the surface of the earth.

The capsule landed in the Caribbean just three miles away from the U.S.S. *Lake Champlain,* an aircraft carrier serving as one of the astronaut's rescue ships. The sailors aboard the carrier watched the giant parachutes lower the capsule gently into the ocean.

NASA

With elation written all over his face, Shepard leaves Freedom Seven **after it has been lowered on the deck of the U.S.S.** Champlain **and after he has retrieved his helmet from the capsule. America was now on its way to the stars.**

Rescue helicopters reached the floating capsule in just a few minutes. A line was lowered and Shepard was hoisted aboard one of the helicopters.

The astronaut grinned broadly at his rescuers. "It's a beautiful day," he exulted. "Boy, what a ride!"

Word of Alan's rescue flashed across the country and around the world. Smiles of satisfaction and pride appeared on the faces of millions of people as they nodded happily. "He did it! *We* did it! America is on its way to the stars."

The helicopter returned to the carrier. When Shepard stepped out, the sailors raised their voices in great cheers that echoed across the empty waters. The astronaut grinned and waved at them.

"I felt a real lump in my throat," he recalls in *We Seven.* "I started for the quarters where the doctors would give me a quick once-over before I flew on to Grand Bahama Island for a full debriefing.

"First, however, I went back to the capsule, which had been lowered gently onto a pile of mattresses on the carrier deck. I wanted to retrieve the helmet I had left behind in the cockpit.

"And I wanted to take one more look at *Freedom Seven.* I was pretty proud of the job that *it* had done, too."

In the next several weeks Alan returned to the United States, to be greeted as the hero that he was. With great skill and personal courage, he had challenged space and won. It was the nation's first great step toward the stars.

America will always honor Alan Shepard, one of the new breed of skymasters.

Appendix

The skymasters whose history-making exploits are dramatized in this book are only a few of the many men who have pitted their courage against the dangers of the sky. Their daring, their determination, and their faith in the future of aviation have been shared by hundreds of other intrepid pioneers who risked death to make the great dream reality.

Following is a brief chronology of the growth of aviation and some of the men who made it possible:

1783—Pilatre de Rozier makes man's first journey into the sky, in a hot-air balloon designed and constructed by Joseph and Etienne Montgolfier of France.

1784—A. J. and M. N. Robert, of France, complete a flight of 150 miles in a hydrogen-filled balloon built by Professor J. A. C. Charles.

1785—Jean-Pierre Blanchard, of France, and Dr. John Jeffries, an American, make the first balloon flight across the English Channel.

1809—Sir George Cayley, of England, describes his research and experiments in the science of heavier-than-air flight. His scientific papers lay the foundation for all modern aerodynamics.

1842—William S. Henson, of England, patents his plans for an "aerial steam carriage." Although the craft was never built, Henson was the first to patent a propeller-driven airplane.

1848—Henson and a fellow Englishman, John Stringfellow, successfully build and fly a model airplane.

1856—Jean-Marie Le Bris, of France, builds a giant glider with a 50-foot wingspan. It completed one short glide, but on the next flight Le Bris lost control of his craft and crashed.

1866—The British Aeronautical Society is organized. This was the first institution of its kind in the world. Its organization gave formal scientific recognition to the world of aviation.

1876—Alphonse Pènaud, of France, patents a design for an amphibious aircraft. This was the first known design calling for a control stick to move both rudder and elevators, retractable landing gear, and a glass cockpit canopy.

1889—Clement Ader, of France, constructs a bat-winged, steam-powered airplane called the *Eole*. The next year, Ader tests the aircraft and claims, but never proves, that it left the ground and flew for 164 feet.

1889—Otto Lilienthal, of Germany, publishes the results of his studies in a book entitled *Bird Flight as a Basis of Aviation*.

1893—Professor John J. Montgomery, of the United States, publishes data on a series of glider experiments he has conducted.

1894—Sir Hiram Maxim, of England, almost becomes the first man to fly a powered, heavier-than-air aircraft. Powered by two 360-horsepower steam engines, with a wingspan of 110 feet, the aircraft lifted clear of its launching tracks, but Maxim turned off the engine rather than lose control of his aircraft. He was satisfied with his experiments at this point and did not fly again.

1896—Otto Lilienthal, the famed German aviator, is killed in a glider crash.

1899—Sir Percy Pilcher, a student of Lilienthal's and one of the most courageous pilots of his time, is killed in a glider crash.

1903—Wilbur and Orville Wright make man's first flight in a self-powered, heavier-than-air airplane at Kitty Hawk, North Carolina.

1904—The Wrights succeed in keeping their aircraft in the air for five minutes and also make the first flight in history in which an airplane left the ground, turned in mid-air and returned to its starting point.

1906—Albert Santos-Dumont makes the first powered airplane flight in Europe.

1908—Glenn Curtiss, one of America's most courageous aviators, wins the first aeronautical speed trophy award presented in the United States.

1909—Louis Bleriot, of France, makes the first airplane flight across the English Channel.

1910—R. M. Fabre makes the first airplane takeoff from water at Port de la Mede, France.

1910—George Chavez, of France, makes the first flight across the Swiss Alps, but is fatally injured in a crash landing at the end of the journey.

1911—Galbraith Perry Rodgers, of the United States, makes the first transcontinental flight across America, flying 3,390 miles in 49 days, from Long Island, New York, to Pasadena, California.

1919—British aviators, Captain John Alcock and Lieutenant A. Whitten Brown, make the first non-stop flight across the Atlantic Ocean, flying from Newfoundland to Ireland, 1,936 miles in 16 hours, and 12 minutes.

1925—Two United States Army aircraft make the first journey around the world, flying from Seattle, Washington, to Seattle, 26,345 miles in 175 days.

1926—U.S. Navy Lieutenant Commander Richard E. Byrd, navigator, and Floyd Bennet, pilot, make the first flight across the North Pole.

1927—Charles A. Lindbergh and his *Spirit of St. Louis* make the first non-stop flight across the Atlantic Ocean from New York to Paris, 3,610 miles in 33 hours, 39 minutes.

1939—The first jet airplane, powered by a turbojet engine, is flown at Rostock, Germany.

1947—First airplane to exceed the speed of sound is flown by American test pilot Charles Yaeger.

1961—Russian Cosmonaut Yuri Gagarin becomes the first man in history to orbit the earth in a space capsule.

1961—American Astronaut Alan B. Shepard becomes the first American to fly a space capsule in outer space.

1962—Lieutenant Colonel John H. Glenn becomes the first American astronaut to orbit the earth in a space capsule.